W9-BRO-930

He knew he should resist—but suddenly he no longer cared...

Celeste stood before him, white-faced and frightened.

"What's happened?" Dan reached out and grasped her shoulders before he could think about what touching her would mean.

"Someone—a man—just called me. He told me to get out of your life. While I still can..."

His hands soothed her shoulders, then swept through her silky hair. He pulled her to his chest, his hand running up and down her back. "It's okay. I'm here." He felt her heart beat, and he bent his head to whisper to her. "I promise no one will harm you." Her safety was the most important thing he could imagine.

She lifted her face and gazed into his eyes. He felt as if he'd stepped from a cliff and was falling, spiraling through the air. He brought his lips down and her mouth opened to accept him. As she pressed her body to his, he knew he should stop. But he was too far gone, too completely under her spell. And though he knew what it might cost, he could no longer deny his need for her....

CAROLINE BURNES

Caroline Burnes has published thirty-five Harlequin Intrigue novels, many of them featuring horses, cowboys, or the black cat detective, Familiar. From the age of four, Caroline wanted to be a cowgirl and write mystery books. Though she is far from a cowgirl, she lives on a farm in south Alabama with six horses, six cats and six dogs. One of the cats, E. A. Poe, is a prototype for Familiar. Although she spent most of her riding career jumping, she recently took up team penning, a sport that demonstrates that cows are far smarter than humans.

CAROLINE BURNES
FAMILIAR VALENTINE

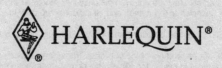

HARLEQUIN®

TORONTO • NEW YORK • LONDON
AMSTERDAM • PARIS • SYDNEY • HAMBURG
STOCKHOLM • ATHENS • TOKYO • MILAN • MADRID
PRAGUE • WARSAW • BUDAPEST • AUCKLAND

If you purchased this book without a cover you should be aware
that this book is stolen property. It was reported as "unsold and
destroyed" to the publisher, and neither the author nor the
publisher has received any payment for this "stripped book."

For B.J. and Helmut,
cat lovers who have been known
to stage midnight rescues.

ISBN 0-373-80959-X

FAMILIAR VALENTINE

Copyright © 1999 by Carolyn Haines

All rights reserved. Except for use in any review, the reproduction or
utilization of this work in whole or in part in any form by any electronic,
mechanical or other means, now known or hereafter invented, including
xerography, photocopying and recording, or in any information storage
or retrieval system, is forbidden without the written permission of the
publisher, Harlequin Enterprises Limited, 225 Duncan Mill Road,
Don Mills, Ontario, Canada M3B 3K9.

All characters in this book have no existence outside the imagination of
the author and have no relation whatsoever to anyone bearing the same
name or names. They are not even distantly inspired by any individual
known or unknown to the author, and all incidents are pure invention.

This edition published by arrangement with Harlequin Books S.A.

® and TM are trademarks of the publisher. Trademarks indicated with
® are registered in the United States Patent and Trademark Office, the
Canadian Trade Marks Office and in other countries.

www.eHarlequin.com

Printed in U.S.A.

CAST OF CHARACTERS

Familiar—He crashes a Valentine charity ball, and finds a lovely damsel in distress in need of a feline detective....

Celeste Levert—She hid behind an assumed name, but couldn't stop the past from catching up to her.

Dan Carson—His dark secrets and dangerous business deals aren't enough to protect his heart from Celeste.

Diana Carson—Dan's mother is a sharp businesswoman—but is she a good judge of character?

Rick Hanson—The FBI agent needed Dan for a sting operation—but whom was he setting up?

Jess Harper—Dan's oldest friend. How much does time change loyalty?

Kenneth Martin—He impersonated a police officer. What else is he lying about?

Phil Norris—A man with an illegal plan—and Dan is the bait.

Trell Sylvest—He was determined to marry Celeste—at any cost?

Shawna Wright—Dan's fiancée died ten years ago—and took with her his right to love another woman.

Chapter One

I've always heard that everything's bigger in Texas, and these cowboy toffs are proving it. So far, this Sweetheart Ball is even bigger than some of the White House bashes Socks, the First Cat, invites me to attend. The flowers are magnificent, there's an orchestra instead of a band, and these Texas women are beauties with a charmin' drawl. Not to mention the food. Champagne, caviar, delicacies of the sea fit for even the likes of me. Ah, shrimp so succulent it makes my whiskers twist, and served on a silver platter. This is life—as I always knew I deserved it. I can't believe my hosts for the week, Ashley and Brak, tried to leave me at home. They should have known that I would not be denied, and it was a simple matter to hide in the van with Ayla. And, voilà, here I am at the party in my sleek black kitty suit.

I see Ayla is having a good time, too. She may be an over-sized feline and a descendent of panther blood, but she likes to show her superior intellect over the humans as much as I do. She and Brak will wow them with the "trained panther floor show."

It's a shame my real humans, Peter and Eleanor, are out of the country. Peter'd love to see his sister,

Ashley, dancing with that brawny hunk of Nordic muscle. This Valentine's Day event is perfect for the lovebirds, and all proceeds are going to the National Heart and Health Association.

In this crush no one will notice one sly cat slipping about, so let me saunter round the room and check out the humans in costume. This theme—Love Through the Centuries—has brought out amazing creativity. Ashley and Brak are Tarzan and Jane. And there's Romeo and Juliet, and a solitary Helen of Troy, and my, my, Adam and Eve. Dig those fig leaves. And that mysterious Mata Hari figure in the veils. She's staring a hole through—the practical joker in the vampire suit? A blond Nosferatu. Very interesting, he's also without a date. No one wanted to attend the ball with the character who rewards his lovers with death. Poor choice of costume, and not very romantic in my book. Oh, I recognize him now. Dan Carson, the big honcho at Carson Dynamics. Ashley and Brak were talking about him last night— the most eligible bachelor in Dallas.

Ah, Mata Hari is slipping back into the crowd. I wonder if she's an old flame of Carson's. She's got a vested interest.

Now what is this bejeweled and feathered wonder coming my way? Oh! If I could clutch my heart, I would. To quote Fred Sanford, "This is the big one." Do my eyes deceive me or is that Aztec goddess a living, breathing woman? I've never seen anyone more stunning, and she's looking right at me and smiling. Heart, be still! If I weren't such a macho kitty, I'd swoon with the pleasure of her glance. I'd drown in those chocolate eyes. I'd die with a purr in *my throat if I were snuggled in those arms. Let me brush against those mile-long legs! Ah, I'm in love!*

But wait a minute. There's something wrong here. There's a glimmer of a tear in those beautiful eyes. And her hands are shaking. I detect that something's amiss.

CELESTE WATCHED the flow of wealthy Texans swirl around her and wondered again what twist of fate had sent her to this ball. She had spent her entire life in Texas, but not among these people, the wealthy icons of Texas society. Not that her family hadn't been well off. She had no idea what her father was worth, but it was plenty. It wasn't the money, it was so much more.

She refused the glass of champagne a waiter offered and began to move through the crowd. Circulate. That was her job. Mix and mingle as a representative of her firm. Even as she thought it she felt a bolstering of her confidence. She had gotten a job at one of the most prestigious investment companies in Texas. And she had earned it, against her family's wishes, because she'd studied hard.

The financial movers and shakers of the Southwest swirled around her and she realized the orchestra was playing a Texas two-step. Women dressed to the nines with diamonds glittering swept by her on the marble dance floor. The Redwing Estate was internationally famous for its lavish ballroom. Everyone seemed to be laughing and having fun. Celeste told herself that she would adjust, that in a matter of time she'd feel at home among these people. She would make it work. Tonight was just difficult. She'd had

the sense all day that something major was going to
happen. Something she couldn't avoid, or escape.

Her gaze rested on the tall man dressed as Dracula.
She felt her blood quicken as her heart did a funny
beat. She had the strangest urge to approach him.
She'd been watching him on and off for a while. He
was an extremely attractive man, and he'd come to
the dance alone, as she had. And he kept looking at
her, too.

Even as she thought it, she caught his glance again.
She stared into his blue eyes, and it was almost as if
he spoke to her. The connection was so strong that it
seemed all background noise disappeared. She took a
hesitant step toward him, drawn by a force she
couldn't resist, but he turned away and resumed his
conversation with a tall, beautiful brunette.

Celeste recognized him then. Dan Carson. His picture had recently been in the Dallas papers, and she
knew a little about him from her intense perusal of
the financial news. He was something of an enigma.
His base of operation was Houston and he had a finger in a lot of financial pies.

Celeste sighed. The one thing she didn't need—
didn't want—was to become interested in a man. Not
now. Not for a long time to come. It would be far too
dangerous for her.

She started toward the ladies' room and bumped
into Mata Hari. Only the woman's eyes showed above
her veiled face, but those eyes sparked with anger.
Celeste started to apologize, but the woman brushed
past her and disappeared among the dancers.

Celeste shook her head and continued to the ladies'
room. She would have preferred a quiet evening,
home alone in her recently furnished cottage. She

still felt like a pretender there, which of course she was. But she knew if she gave herself a chance and a little time, she'd become Celeste Sanchez, financial wizard. She just had to be patient, keep her profile low and concentrate on making the new life she'd chosen work.

She saw the black cat and felt a spike of pleasure. She adored cats. And this was one elegant-looking feline. And so well mannered that he was attending a party. "Kitty, kitty." She called him over to her and bent to scratch him under the chin. He responded with a deep rumble of a purr, and Celeste caught the attention of a waiter.

"Does the cat live here?" she asked.

"I'm not sure, ma'am. He seems to have wandered in." He looked at the cat, who gave him back a golden stare. "He's well behaved, and we thought it would be less of a problem if we ignored him. Is he bothering you?"

"Absolutely not," Celeste answered. "He's magnificent."

"I hope he isn't left here after the party." The waiter frowned. "I've never seen a pet on the estate." He nodded and hurried away.

Celeste scratched Familiar behind the ears. "I'd love to have a kitty like you." She felt someone staring at her, and for a moment she wondered if Dan Carson was nearby. Her gaze lifted and she saw dark eyes boring into hers.

For a split second, Celeste was frozen with panic. She did not know the man, not personally. But she recognized his Roma eyes and knew her father had sent him. She wouldn't go home! She wouldn't! She felt tears spring to her eyes and she abruptly turned away and headed for an exit out of the mansion. She had a right to live her own life, and not even her father, the leader of her people, could make her marry a man she didn't love.

DAN CARSON shrugged his shoulders and the cape billowed around his lean hips. With a mock bow, he excused himself from the beautiful brunette and turned back to where he'd last seen the woman in the Aztec getup. He had no intention of approaching her—not on his life, or hers. There were dozens of beautiful women at the ball, but there was something about her that instantly drew his attention, and his interest. He felt as if he knew her. Not casually or socially, but with a deep, personal knowledge that was both exciting and a little frightening. Therefore, she was off-limits.

But it wouldn't hurt to look at her.

He felt the old familiar anger build, and he swallowed it back. Now wasn't the time to moan about his personal problems. He'd come to The Sweetheart Ball to conduct business. His romantic complications would have to wait.

At first he didn't see the woman, and then he noticed she was bending down to stroke a black cat. Imagine, a cat at a formal ball. And not only the house cat—there was also a black panther mingling with the guests, a part of some floor show for later. The sponsors of the dance outdid themselves every year.

He knew he shouldn't stare at the woman in the Aztec dress, but he couldn't help himself. He saw her watching a man leaning against the wall. The man wore a tuxedo, no costume. Dan examined him more closely and realized that he might have assumed the man was hired security. Except for the way his gaze burned into the woman. Instantly Dan tensed.

The woman went completely still, and then it looked as if she might cry. Instead she turned and hurried away. As Dan watched, the man began to follow her.

"Dan Carson!"

Dan's attention was diverted from the woman as the voice he recognized turned out to belong to the man he'd been waiting to meet.

"Jess." He took the extended hand and shook it firmly. Then he smiled. "It's good to see you."

"It is indeed." Jess pumped his hand. "I hear good things about Carson Dynamics."

"If half of what you hear is true, I'll be in good shape," Dan said. He glanced across the crowded room to see that the Aztec goddess was heading for an exit. Dan caught the movement of the man. It looked as if he were following her. Lover's spat? More than likely. Whatever it was, it didn't involve him. He had to keep his mind on business.

"Is something wrong?" Jess Harper asked, his eyes narrowing.

"Some woman," Dan said, giving a sardonic grin.

"You haven't changed since high school," Jess said, and then he colored. "I didn't mean that the way it sounded, Dan. I know all of that with Shawna…"

"Forget it," Dan said, a bit more brusquely than he intended. "I'm sorry. I guess I'm a little raw, still." There was no possible way he could explain.

Jess nodded. "It was awful. Even though it's been ten years, I still think about that day. I've never seen you so happy, and then so…" He patted Dan's shoulder. "But you're looking fine. We were all worried that you would break, but..." Jess grasped both of his shoulders and smiled. "It's damn good to see you after all this time. Now, what about this urgent business deal that couldn't wait until after the ball?"

Dan smiled. "I'm looking for some investors. I thought you might be able to put together some people with money. Folks who wouldn't ask too many questions if they had a chance to make a real profit."

Jess's mouth tightened. "I never figured you to do anything even slightly shady. What's this about?"

Dan had expected some resistance but he didn't think it would last. He'd done his homework. He knew his old friend Jess Harper was in financial straits. "I'm connected to an oil supplier, but I need cash to pay for it. Between the two of us, we can get it into the States and the refineries without too much difficulty." Dan knew that Jess understood everything he left unspoken—that the oil was foreign, that it was illegal, that they stood to make a great deal of money.

Jess stared at him. "I shouldn't ask where this oil is coming from, should I?"

"No." Dan said it with feeling.

"How soon?"

"I need to know by the first of next week. Then I want a face-to-face. I want to see who I'm doing business with, and I want to see their money. Cash."

"How much?" Jess asked, frowning.

"I need twenty million up front to buy the oil."

"Twenty million." Jess's eyebrows showed his appreciation for that sum of money.

"We can sell it for double what we pay for it, guaranteed. We'll turn twenty million in less than two weeks." Dan saw the possibilities working on his friend and he turned away, swept by a sudden prick of shame. In better days Jess Harper would have walked away from this deal. He would have been disgusted by the offer and ashamed for Dan's involvement. "Can you put it together?" Dan pressed.

"I'll call you tomorrow night about a meeting," Jess said. His suntanned face was furrowed. He stepped closer to Dan to avoid the swirling costume of a woman as she passed.

"I'll be in Houston. I've got an early meeting so I'm flying out at daybreak. I'll be at the main office." To do the deal, Dan needed Jess, but he also hoped that his old friend, the man who would have been best man at his wedding, would never pick up the phone and call.

Suddenly Dan found himself deafened by the music and the chatter and the laughter of the crowd. It was as if someone turned the volume up on the party. He nodded at Jess and turned on his heel.

Though he tried not to, he looked for the Aztec goddess. But she was gone. Vanished. What caught his eye was the panther, the sleek creature that had been padding around the dance floor like an over-size pussycat.

He watched the big cat closely, fascinated by such grace and power. She stood poised at a window, looking out into the night. She seemed to vibrate with intensity, and the tip of her tail twitched ever so slightly.

Dan recognized the posture—a stalking attitude. He heard the big Nordic man calling to the panther, but she completely ignored him.

The cat's intensity held Dan's attention. Her tail twitched once, furiously, and she turned her golden gaze on Dan. Her pupils dilated, then narrowed. When she jumped out the window, Dan followed in a movement so smooth that no one even noticed. The idea that the panther had urged him to follow was nuts, but it was a compulsion Dan couldn't ignore.

MY GODDESS is headed toward the exit. She's subtle, but I'm a TO, that's Trained Observer, and I notice things like a woman crying and leaving a room.

I think I'll sashay after her, check it out. Could be something as simple as her date didn't bring her champagne. Or it could be something serious. One thing I've learned about humans is that they never react in a reasonable fashion. They face death with no elevation in heartbeat, but if they find a cat walking on their counter, they go ballistic. Absolutely irrational creatures.

She bypassed the ladies' room, and she's walking a lot faster. My eyes tell me to enjoy this vision of shimmering blue gown and the flash of a long, elegant leg. But my brain tells me that this woman is in trouble. It's a good thing I'm here.

She's headed for the gardens. Brak and Ashley were talking about the fabulous grounds of the Redwing Estate. Now I'll get to see them firsthand. Rose gardens, pools and the maze. Ever since The Shining *I've had a little difficulty with mazes and topiaries, but I'm sure I'll get over it. Now, let me scoot out the door before it shuts! Yes, and we're into the Texas night.*

Looking around, one wouldn't realize that we're in the middle of one of the biggest cities in America. This estate is so removed, so private. And they say money can't buy happiness. Perhaps not love, but happiness? I'm reserving judgment.

There she goes, into the maze. And she's looking back over her shoulder as if… The door to the house is opening. Someone is following her. He's backlit and he's big. Oh, hell, now she's running. And right into the maze. Not the smartest decision, honey, but never fear, I'm right behind you.

CELESTE HAD no idea where she was going, flight was her only option. The avenue of shrubs she entered was two feet over her head, a narrow path that offered no hiding place, only a series of junctions. She turned left and ran. Footsteps pursued her.

The dress was tight and her heels too high for running, but she couldn't stop long enough to get rid of them. She couldn't stop for anything. She turned again, aware that she'd lost all sense of direction. She didn't care. She made another right turn and almost skidded to a stop. The statue of Venus rising out of the sea almost frightened her to death. In the moonlight, she saw that the Roman goddess had been decorated for the party and held a heart-shaped wreath of red roses.

Celeste moved toward the statue, wondering if she could somehow find a hiding place. But the base wasn't large enough to hide her. She touched the cool marble, needing to rest for a moment and catch her breath. But this wasn't the place. She started to run again.

She'd rather be lost in the maze than confront one of her father's henchmen. Or worse, someone sent by Trell Sylvest.

At the thought of the man her father had selected

for her to marry, Celeste felt a burst of anger, and it was the jolt she needed to keep her moving. Her side felt as if a blade were knifing into it, and her lungs burned with the effort of running. No matter how hard or fast she ran, she still heard someone following her. And the maze offered no place to hide. The shrubs, trimmed and manicured, were solid as a wall.

"Meow!"

She was about to give up when she heard the cat. She looked down to find the cat from the party, running at her side.

"Meow." He gazed up at her with golden eyes that seemed to reassure her.

Celeste continued running. She stopped abruptly when the narrow path ended in a small circle. A lover's seat rested in its center, decorated with a bower of carnations. Cupid presided over the love seat, bow drawn taut and a sharp arrow aimed right at Celeste's heart.

In the silver light of the moon, the cherubic archer and the flowers looked eerie. Celeste backed away and searched the enclosure for another way out, but there wasn't one. The only exit was the way she'd entered.

Crying out on a muffled sob, Celeste started back the way she'd come. She'd gone less than ten feet when the man appeared at the other end of the passage. He'd been running, but he slowed to a walk as he came toward her.

"Leave me alone," Celeste warned him.

"I've come to take you home."

Her worst fears were confirmed. Somehow her father, or Trell, had discovered her new identity. They'd followed her to Dallas. Now they'd trapped her and intended to take her home.

"I'm not going with you," she said, clenching her hands then finally pulling off the horrid shoes. She clutched one, the only weapon she could find. As he advanced toward her, she crouched and held the shoe. "I'm a grown woman. I'm twenty-seven years old, and I'm an American citizen. I don't have to go home with you, and I don't intend to. If you try to force me, you're a party to kidnapping. I promise, I'll press charges."

"These matters do not involve the *gajikane* police. This is only for our people."

"I love my people and my family, but I will not be sold into a marriage. Never." Celeste took a deep breath. "Never."

"Miss Levert, you must return home."

She heard the determination in his voice. "I'll never go with you. I would rather die."

The man shook his head sadly. "There are many types of death. Choose with great caution, because once done, it can never be reversed."

Chapter Two

"Your father wants to talk to you." The man circled closer. "The least you can do is talk to him. He is certain you don't understand your responsibility in this matter. You have the ring. He is sure you will listen to him."

"I have nothing to say to my father. Deliver that message. I'm pursuing my own life. I ask nothing of him except that he leave me alone." Her hand went instinctively to her chest. She could feel the man's eyes on her and knew that he was searching for the ring. "Stay away from me."

"You're Ramone Levert's daughter. His only heir." The man stepped closer. "And you stole the ring."

"I'm a grown woman with my whole life ahead of me and I stole nothing." She forced her hand down. The ring was snugly fitted into her dress. It hung from a chain around her neck, and she would never give it up. Although she might not want to lead the life her father had chosen for her, she was still a Levert, still a member of her clan. The ring was hers, by birthright.

"When you disobey your father, you are also disobeying the ruler of our people, your king."

"I'm not going home."

Celeste thought she was prepared for the attack, but when the man lunged across the small enclosure toward her, she instinctively stumbled backward. The grass was soft and freshly cut, and her foot slipped in the dew that coated the tender blades. The man grasped her around the waist and they went down together. Celeste felt as if she'd been punched in the stomach. The weight of the big man knocked the air from her lungs.

"Aaiiyee!" the man was suddenly screaming and slapping at his back. He rolled off Celeste and jumped to his feet. As he began to spin, Celeste saw that the black cat had jumped onto his back and was riding him.

"Get the cat!" The man screamed at her. Celeste didn't move. Out of the corner of her eye, she saw another movement, this time black on black. When she realized what it was, she really couldn't breath. With one bound, Ayla was at the man's side. Her enormous paw swatted out at him, knocking him backward into the maze. The other cat sprang free.

Before Celeste could do anything, another figure darted into the clearing. Cape billowing, Dan Carson rushed at her attacker. The two men fought as Celeste watched in horror. They traded several blows, but at last her attacker connected one solid swing to Dan's jaw. It was enough to knock Dan off balance and into the statue of Cupid. Dan gave a surprised cry of pain and the attacker turned and fled. In the distance a man called Ayla's name, and the panther melted into the darkness as quietly as she'd arrived.

Celeste hurried toward her protector as he stumbled to the love seat. "Are you okay?" she asked, sitting beside him. Against the starched white of his shirt, she could see blood on his chest. Her hand instinctively went there to apply pressure. She was terrified, the wound was exactly over his heart. Had he been stabbed? She hadn't seen a knife, but the moonlight wasn't the best, and though the attacker had appeared to work for her father, he might have been sent by Trell. The men who worked for Trell Sylvest were rumored to be very good with weapons. She forced her panic down, and against the pressure of her palm she felt his heart beat strong and regular.

"I'm fine. Are you hurt?" he asked.

"Not at all," she said. He did sound okay, his voice a deep baritone that was like a touch. "He didn't hurt me."

"We have to call the police." Dan rubbed his jaw. "What did he want?"

Celeste wasn't prepared to tell the truth, and she wasn't very good at lying. The one thing she didn't want was police. "I'm not exactly certain," she said. "He was staring at me in the ballroom. When I came outside, I realized someone was following me. I panicked and ran into the maze." That was all true. She just managed to avoid answering his real question. She realized that she was sitting so close to Dan that her legs brushed his. Her dress had torn and the slit now extended almost to her waist.

Dan seemed to notice the tear at the same time she did. He looked down at her long, exposed leg, then up into her eyes. For a split second their gazes held.

Celeste wanted him to kiss her. It was unreasonable and dangerous, but she wanted it nonetheless. For the past two years she'd wondered if something was wrong with her. It was time she fell in love, time she began to seek her own man—or in her case, accept the one her father had chosen. But she'd been so focused on learning, and none of the men she knew had stirred her. But now? Her lips parted and she took a shallow breath. She saw his gaze move from her eyes to her lips and she knew that he wanted to kiss her, too. Desire arced between them.

For Celeste, it was as if nothing else had happened before this moment. She was alone with a stranger in Cupid's garden. Moonlight bathed the man's features, gilding his blond curls with silver. She realized she didn't know anything about him. It didn't matter. The only thing that mattered was the feeling rushing through her. This man had touched her in a way that no one had before. She had never been so alive. He felt it, too. She could see it in his blue eyes, an awareness that something extraordinary had passed between them. He leaned toward her and she began to close her eyes, wanting only his kiss.

"Meow!" The black cat jumped onto the love seat, his sharp claws sinking into Dan's thigh.

"Ouch!" Dan looked down at the cat.

To Celeste, it was as if a magic spell had been broken. She came fully to her senses and used her hand to pull the torn pieces of her dress together. What had she been thinking? What had happened to her? She was a woman of reason and intelligence, and she'd almost thrown herself into the arms of a man dressed as Dracula. Embarrassed, Celeste finally looked up and met the stranger's gaze. As she watched, she could almost see the wall he erected between his emotions and her. His shoulders squared and he sat up. Where there had been electricity between them, there was now empty space.

DAN FELT AS if he'd been hit in the head with a blunt object. Thank goodness for the cat. If he'd actually kissed the lush lips of the woman he'd felt so strangely compelled to rescue, he knew his life would have changed. That could mean only one thing, and it wasn't good.

He'd had one lesson in true love and he never wanted another. He didn't think he could survive such a review.

"Meow!" The cat patted his leg, demanding attention. Dan had a sensation of uneasiness. He'd followed a panther to rescue this woman, and now a black cat was on the scene. This was definitely something out of the norm. Celeste's voice captured his attention.

"You're bleeding. Did he cut you?"

Although the question was asked in a soft, controlled voice, he wished the woman had not spoken. There was the hint of some place exotic in her voice, a land of warmth and sun. He looked at her again and saw the worry in her dark brown eyes. Her lashes were thick, and as he lowered his gaze he saw a pulse in her throat.

"Excuse me," she said, touching him lightly on the chest. "Are you cut?" Her palm pressed against his beating heart, and Dan felt as if a balm had been laid on old wounds.

He realized she was referring to the blood on his shirt. He knew the attacker hadn't cut him—there'd been no knife. He'd injured himself on the point of Cupid's arrow. His hand went to the wound. "It's superficial. Just a scrape," he said, rising. The chest wound gave a painful throb. Dan knew he had to get out of the maze. His attraction for the woman was not to be trusted.

"Thank you so much," she said, rising as well. She extended a slender hand. "I'm Celeste Sanchez."

"Dan Carson," he said, taking her hand. Once again he had an overpowering urge, this time to engulf her small hand in his larger one.

"How did you know I was in danger?" she asked.

Dan didn't have an answer. "Actually, I was following the, uh, the panther." Saying it out loud sounded really dumb.

"Ayla," Celeste nodded. "That's her name. I was talking with her owners earlier. She's magnificent."

"Meow!"

At the demanding noise from the domestic cat, Celeste laughed and scooped him into her arms. "I'm not forgetting you, little one. You fought like a tiger to save me."

Dan quirked an eyebrow.

"It's true," Celeste said, stroking the cat. "He jumped on the man who attacked me. He was the first surprise of the night for that man." She laughed softly. "The panther was the second, and you were the icing on the cake."

Dan could see that she was quickly regaining her equilibrium from the events of the evening. He smiled. "We should go back inside." He looked down at her gown. "I'm sure there's someone here who can repair your dress. At least so you can enjoy the remainder of the evening."

He saw a flicker of distress cross her face, but then

she composed her features. "I think I'd prefer to go home."

"Then let me give you a lift." He knew better, but he couldn't help himself. The more he fought his attraction to this woman, the more he found he could not let her slip away from him.

"That's very kind, but I can call a cab. You should go back inside and finish the evening." Celeste stroked the cat in her arms.

"No, I insist," Dan said. "And on the way to your place we can stop and report this attack to the police."

Still holding the cat, Celeste shook her head. "No police."

"The man attacked you. It should be reported." Dan spoke softly, wondering at the fear on Celeste Sanchez's face. Did she have something to hide from the authorities?

"No police," she said more firmly. "It was probably an attempt to rob me. The man is gone. It's best to let it go."

"He could have killed you," Dan argued. "If the cats or I hadn't come along, there's no telling what might have happened to you."

"Nothing happened." Celeste's hand touched his arm. "Please. No police."

Dan tried to ignore the pleading look in her eyes, but he couldn't. "Okay, no police." He summoned his willpower. "On one condition. Tell me what's going on here. Obviously you knew the man."

He saw her hesitate, and when she looked down at the cat again, he thought she might lie. But then she looked up at him and spoke.

"That man knows my...family. I ran away to start

a new life. I couldn't stand it anymore, the way I was living. I have a talent for numbers, so I mostly taught myself about the financial market and I moved here to Dallas to start over. But now they've found me. He was going to try and make me go home.'' Celeste's voice broke. "I won't go back there. I won't.''

Dan immediately suspected an abusive husband. "Do you have children?" he asked.

"No." Celeste looked at him, startled. "No children.'' Her eyes widened.

"Ms. Sanchez, if your husband or family is hurting you, you can report them to the police.'' Dan felt as if he were on thin ice. What he knew about domestic violence he'd learned from cop shows on television. But he'd seen this woman attacked, by someone who was apparently a hired hand. This was not a situation he could turn his back on.

Celeste took a breath and confirmed his suspicions. "I can't go to the police.''

Dan understood, on one level. No woman, or man, would want to admit that someone she loved was abusing her. It was the worst betrayal. "Okay," he said. "No police.''

The idea came to him suddenly. "You're good with money?''

Celeste nodded. "I work for Stevens and Lynch. I've been there three months and I just got a raise. My work is satisfactory.'' Her voice almost broke. "But I can't stay—I'll have to move. I'll have to start over somewhere else.''

He could see that her future looked pretty bleak to her. She was being stalked. "I have a proposal," he heard himself saying. The words seemed to come out of nowhere. Dan wasn't in the habit of rescuing abused women or offering jobs. "Come to work for me."

"What?" Celeste frowned.

He couldn't stop himself. "My company is Carson Dynamics. We do a number of things, some which are very much in line with the services offered by Stevens and Lynch. Come and work for me in the Houston office. My plane leaves in the morning at seven sharp. Have your things ready at six and, I'll send a driver to pick you up."

CELESTE FELT as if a prayer had been answered— several prayers. Dan Carson wasn't going to make her go to the police. Which was something she absolutely could not do under any circumstances. The Roma people almost never involved the authorities in their business, especially not in something of this personal a nature. She felt guilty for letting Dan believe she had fled an abusive husband, but it made for a more credible story than the truth.

Not only had she escaped the law, she'd been of- fered a job out of Dallas. Houston wasn't on the other side of the world, but it was a big city, and with a secure job, she could lose herself in the masses. She had to.

The only thing that troubled her was her extreme reaction to the man who would now be her boss. She'd never met anyone who affected her so. But she could control herself.

"Thank you, Mr. Carson," she said. "I know you don't know anything about me or my abilities, but I promise you that I'm good at what I do, and I'll prove myself."

Dan's smile was warm. "I'm sure you will. I'll call

the office when I get back to my hotel. What division are you working in?''

"Personal investments,'' she said. This was all happening so fast. Would it be possible for her to pack her clothes and start over again in less than twelve hours? The answer was yes.

When she'd first run away from home, it had taken long months of planning. She'd had to slip around her father to attend classes on financial management, and had called on her girlfriends to help cover her tracks. She'd been free for only three months and already she'd been run to ground. But this time, in Houston, she'd be more careful.

"Good. I think you'll like Carson Dynamics. If not, or whenever you think you want to move along, I'll help you find work. If you're a hard worker and have a little talent and luck, you'll find that in a matter of months you'll be able to write your own ticket.''

Celeste felt her mouth lift into the first real smile of the evening. She was confused about her family, her future and her choices in life, but there was one thing she was absolutely sure of, and that was her career. "I intend to do just that,'' she said. "Now I think I need to get home.''

To her surprise, the black cat suddenly leaped into her arms. "I'd almost forgotten about you,'' Celeste said. She looked back at Dan. "Do you think he belongs to the Redwing family?''

"He was at the party, so I'm assuming he's a member of the family or at least a paying guest.'' Dan smiled. He could see Celeste was worried about the cat. Her own future was uncertain, but she still wanted to make sure the cat was okay.

"I'll check at the house,'' Celeste said. She hesitated. "If he doesn't belong to anyone, may I bring him on the plane? I can't leave him. He tried to save my life." Her words rushed out.

Dan eyed the cat. Big gold eyes returned his stare, as if the cat were taking his measure. "Sure," he said. "Just as long as you don't want to bring the panther."

UH-OH, METHINKS the plot has moved too fast, too soon. Something tells me our Golden Goddess hasn't been exactly straightforward with Dracula. Sometimes I wonder about humans. How is it possible that they've become the dominant species? It hardly seems fair that a prehensile thumb means more than brainpower.

I mean, look at this situation. Dracula arrives to find this woman under attack. She feeds him some story about running away from home—a story that even I can detect is chock-full of holes—and he offers her a job in Houston. Never checks her credentials. Nothing. I think when he punctured himself on Cupid's arrow, he did some brain damage as well. And really, it was almost as if he deliberately threw himself on that arrow.

There's only one thing for certain in all of this— Golden Goddess, or GG as I like to call her, isn't going to Houston alone.

This is a job for Familiar, supersleuth. Now I just have to figure a way to get word to Ashley and Brak that I'm going to Houston and they shouldn't worry about me. Of course, they don't know I'm here at the party, and I can't let them see me. Once I'm in Houston, I'll send them word that I'm okay and on the job.

Chapter Three

Celeste kept her back straight as she walked beside Dan to the door of her home. The sense of being followed had stayed with her during the ride, and she swung around to examine the quiet street. There was no traffic. None at all. She and Dan seemed to be alone in the cool night.

Her small cottage was located in one of Dallas's older residential neighborhoods. She could sense Dan evaluating it and felt a flicker of concern. She could almost follow his thoughts. How did a lone woman who'd run away from her abusive husband get enough money to rent a house in such an upscale neighborhood? She risked a glance at Dan.

"Nice place," he said levelly.

"Thank you." She was glad to have the black cat in her arms. The staff at Redwing had assured her that the cat didn't belong on the premises. They'd also made it clear that after the party, he wouldn't be allowed to remain there. And Familiar had clung to her as if he were attached with Velcro fur.

As she unlocked the front door, she kept one eye on the shrubs beside the small porch. She couldn't shake the feeling she was being watched. Ramone

Levert didn't like his subordinates to return with unfinished business.

She shifted the door open and hesitated. The polite
thing to do would be to invite Dan inside, but she was
reluctant to do so. He had such an intense effect on
her, and one that she couldn't afford to explore further. She knew trouble when she smelled it—she
didn't have to have her nose rubbed in it. Once she
reached Houston and got settled, she'd begin looking
for a different job. Dan would understand—would un-
doubtedly be relieved.

"Be at the airport at six," Dan said, handing her
a piece of paper. "This is the gate number. My limo
will pick you up, but if you have any trouble, show
this and someone will make sure you get to my
plane."

Celeste took the paper. "Thank you, Mr. Carson."
At last she met his gaze. His blue eyes were tired and
she felt a pang of remorse. There was so much more
she wanted to say. She wanted to tell Dan Carson the
truth. It was unfair, letting him help her under false
pretenses. But truth was a luxury she couldn't afford
at the moment. "I don't know why you followed Ayla
out to the maze, and I don't know why you decided
to help me. Somehow, I'll make you glad you did."

Dan smiled. "Do a good job at the office and figure
out a way to make your life safe. That'll be thanks
enough."

"I'll see you at six," Celeste said, and closed the
door before she could give in to the need to confess.
She locked the door and leaned against it, the cat still
in her arms. "If he only knew what I'm running
from," she whispered, "he wouldn't help me. He'd

despise me.'' Suddenly she wondered if freedom and independence were worth the price she was having to pay.

DAN PUT THE CAR in drive and smoothly pulled away from the curb in front of Celeste's house. Even though the evening was officially over, Celeste Sanchez was still very much on his mind. As headlights glared in the rearview mirror, he adjusted it and pulled smoothly into the main road.

He headed toward the downtown hotel he'd made his headquarters since flying into Dallas. The city had been a special surprise to him. He'd been away for a long time, a self-imposed exile that had dimmed the painful memories a little. As he looked at the familiar skyline, he smiled at the memory of his childhood impression of Dallas. The city had reminded him of the Land of Oz.

His thoughts were bittersweet as he remembered Dorothy's desire to return home. He'd always believed he would never come back.

But then circumstances had put him in a position where he couldn't say no.

His hands tightened on the wheel and he turned a corner, glancing back at the quiet street he was leaving behind. Celeste Sanchez had money. Judging by her looks, she'd inherited it. She had the dress and attitude of a woman born to the finer things. And she was very, very smart. Stevens and Lynch was one of the most successful and competitive companies in the South. They only hired the pick of the litter.

So, he wasn't worried about offering Celeste a job. He was worried about her being in the office every day where he would see her, until finally he yielded to the impulse to kiss her. And that was something he could never allow. Some folks had the Midas Touch and others had green thumbs. Dan's touch produced another result—heartache or death. He could not allow his fascination for Celeste Sanchez to go any further.

The solution was simple and easy to accomplish. He wouldn't be in the office much.

He turned the car onto the interstate and toward his hotel.

As he drove across town, he found himself looking for the landmarks that were personal to him. He'd once lived in Dallas. He'd been a young man then, just out of college and determined to set the world on its ear. He smiled as he remembered the enthusiasm that had been so much a part of his circle of friends. Jess Harper had been with him, and a handful of others, all business school graduates. They'd been eager to get into the real world and make money—to take risks and reap the rewards. God, they had been such brash young men.

And Shawna had been right with them.

Dan's grip tightened on the wheel as he turned the car and his thoughts in another direction.

He pulled into the hotel, tossed the keys to the valet and hurried to his room. He slid out of the tuxedo and cape and picked up the phone. In a moment he was listening to the ring in Washington, D.C.

"Hanson here."

Dan skipped the greetings. "I made contact with Harper. He's going to call me tonight to set up the meeting."

"Very good."

Dan could hear the pleasure in the CIA agent's voice and it only fueled his feeling of helplessness.

"When this is finished, I'm done with you." His anger at being forced to put his old friend in such a bad position was directed at Rick Hanson, the man who'd conceived this great sting operation.

"You bring in the men I want and I'll be glad to see the last of you." Hanson's voice eased. "If it makes you feel better, you can think about what you're doing for your country. If we don't plug this oil leak, the foreign policies Congress enacts aren't worth the paper they're written on."

Dan understood that the web he was caught in had international implications. He just didn't like it. He was a businessman who loved risk. Putting his money on the line was an everyday fact of life. But it was his money and his risk. He didn't like involving innocents—even if the man in question had already stepped over the line once or twice.

"I'll do what I agreed. I don't have to like it. But I want something from you."

Hanson's voice took on an edgy tone. "You're not exactly in a position to make demands. What do you want?"

"I need some background on a woman named Celeste Sanchez."

"This isn't exactly the time to start a romantic encounter," Hanson said briskly.

"This is business. I need to know if her husband has a police record."

Hanson sighed. "Okay. I'll get this for you. But keep focused on your assignment."

"Don't worry. I'll do what I promised," Dan said, hanging up the phone before the CIA agent could respond.

Dan took a hot shower and let the pounding water

ease the tension in his shoulders. His chest bore the evidence of Cupid's arrow, and he ruefully touched it. If he were a man who believed in omens, he'd find this one unnerving, especially after his reaction to Celeste Sanchez.

As he lay on the king-size bed and tried to sleep, his thoughts drifted to her. His attraction had begun at the dance. Her exotic costume had drawn his attention, and then he'd connected with her gaze. He couldn't begin to figure out what had happened after that. It was something over which he'd had no control. It was as if his body had begun to act on instinct. He'd almost kissed her, a woman who was a total stranger.

And she'd almost kissed him back.

And Celeste Sanchez, with her highborn manner, didn't strike him as a woman who kissed strangers in garden mazes. He couldn't help smiling as he thought about her. The Aztec goddess costume had been perfection.

But what about her husband? Well, he'd know soon enough. The CIA could certainly manage a simple assignment like that.

CELESTE PUT THE envelopes in the mailbox. She'd paid all of her bills and cancelled her utilities. She'd had only an hour's sleep, but she'd taken care of everything. She couldn't afford loose ends such as power companies trying to dun her for unpaid bills or a landlord who was angry over her breaking a lease. Maybe it didn't matter now, since her father had obviously found her. But paying her bills for another month might buy her a little time.

"Come on, Kitty," she said, calling the black cat.

He'd been a source of comfort. Once again she was moving to a new place, establishing a new life. At least the cat would be something alive and happy to see her at the end of the day. She had another guilt pang. He belonged to someone, but who? And if she didn't take him, what would she do with him?

She moved her bags to the porch in anticipation of the car Dan Carson said he would send. When she went back in the house, she found the cat beside the telephone, meowing into the receiver as if he were carrying on a conversation.

"Isn't that cute," she said, picking him up and cuddling him to her chest. "Time to go." She replaced the phone. As she walked to the yard the limo pulled up and the driver got out to load her bags.

Celeste turned and took one last look at her small house, the place that only hours ago had seemed safe. A sudden wave of hopelessness made her shoulders sag. How long could she keep running? And in the end, would she ever escape? She had a compelling urge to call her mother, but Maria Levert had made her position perfectly clear on the issue of Celeste's marriage. Maria agreed with her husband—Celeste would do as she was told. To call home would only put her mother in the middle of a fight where there could be no winners. No, Celeste had chosen independence, and now she had it in spades.

SO WE'RE RIDING to the airport in high style. Yes indeed, Dan Carson is a man who knows how to live the good life. I got a call through to Ashley, and she heard my voice. She's a good border patrol agent, and she'll have the call traced in a matter of minutes. But we'll be long gone before she gets here. At least she knows I'm okay. I wish there was some way I could let her know that I'm making this trip voluntarily, and that I haven't been catnapped!

Perhaps Ayla can communicate with Brak. They have that bond, and she knows where I am. I'll make another attempt to call as soon as possible.

I made a cursory investigation of Celeste's digs, and I didn't find anything. Which may be a clue in itself. There are no photos of her with her husband, no family pictures, nothing personal at all. It's as if Ms. Sanchez were born only a week or so ago. I find this intriguing, and puzzling. And last night I caught some of the conversation between her and her assailant. Her people, her king, her father—all very archaic sounding. And very interesting. This black kitty has bought into the mystery and this luxury ride. I wonder if there's some caviar on this yacht of a car?

There's the private airport, and that must be Dan's plane. I'd say that Carson Dynamics is very, very successful.

Hmm, since I haven't been officially hired on this case, I'm wondering how I can present a bill for my services. I'm sure I'll figure out a way. But I'll worry about that tomorrow.

DAN STEPPED FORWARD to greet the limo. He'd had a sleepless night and had convinced himself that Celeste Sanchez could not possibly be the compelling woman he'd imagined. He was eager to open the car door and confront her to prove to himself that his reaction to her had been the result of moonlight, danger and the champagne he'd drunk.

As she stepped out of the car, though, he knew he'd only managed to fool himself. She wore a navy blue business suit and her long dark hair was up in a French twist. But though she'd downplayed her physical beauty, he felt as if he'd been slugged, hard, in the chest. And to make matters worse, the wound he'd received from the arrow tip began to itch.

"Ms. Sanchez," he said, assisting her to the steps of the plane. She held the black cat in her arms. At the foot of the steps she hesitated, finally looking up to meet his gaze.

Dan took a deep breath. "It's going to be okay," he said.

She smiled at him, and Dan caught a glimpse of the vulnerability behind the veneer of independence that she'd erected. She was afraid, and yet she was moving forward. He had to admire her courage. "Thank you," she whispered. "I'm sure it will."

"Meow," the cat agreed.

"Have you named him yet?" Dan asked.

Celeste shook her head. "I didn't want to. In case his owners claimed him."

"Looks like there's not much chance of that now."

"I suppose not," Celeste agreed. "My father always thought black cats were bad luck. Maybe I should call him Lucky."

The cat pinned his ears back.

"He doesn't like that name," Dan said, amazed at the cat's ability to display his likes and dislikes. "Let's get onboard and we can figure out what to call him."

In a matter of moments, Celeste's luggage was stowed and she was seated in the spacious cabin. Dan sat across from her and found that in the early light of morning, she was more beautiful than he'd remembered. Soon the small jet was airborne and he found himself enjoying his conversation with Celeste.

In a short time, they established an easy camaraderie, and he found that he was relaxing. She was beautiful, but at last he had his reaction to her under control.

"Let me get some coffee," he said.

"I can make it," Celeste offered.

"Kip took care of it," Dan said, rising. "He's got a fetish for this particular type of coffee, so he always has a fresh pot made whenever we go anyplace."

He was halfway to the small kitchen when the plane dropped out from under his feet. For a second he hung in midair, then the plane dipped again and Dan smashed against the ceiling. He grabbed the back of a seat and managed to hold on as the plane careened into a spin. Small items flew about the cabin, and there was the sound of glass smashing. A feeling of dread crept along Dan's spine. At last the plane leveled out and he was able to stand. His first concern was Celeste.

"What is it?" Celeste asked. Her seat belt was still buckled and she had suffered no injuries. She held the cat in her arms. Both looked shaken but okay.

"I don't know," Dan said, heading to the cockpit. "But I'll find out soon enough."

His pilot, Kip Dees, had been with him for the past ten years and was the best in the business. Dan felt a twinge of anxiety as he pushed aside the petition that separated the cockpit from the plane.

"Kip, what's going…" The words died in his throat. Kip made a feeble attempt to grasp the stick, but his hand missed. The plane began another sickening drop.

This time Dan had nothing to hold on to and he slammed into the side of the plane as it lurched right. "Kip!" Dan called. "Kip!"

The pilot made an effort to respond. He lurched against his seat belt and fumbled at the control panel. For a brief instant, the plane righted and Dan was able to grasp the back of the pilot's seat.

The plane went into another gut-twisting drop before Dan could do anything else.

"Dan?" Celeste's panicked voice came from the passenger area.

"It's okay, Celeste!" Dan called out as he held on to the back of the seat while attempting to gain control of the stick. The plane was powerful and fast and fought against him, but he finally managed to level it out. He turned to find Celeste, pale and big-eyed, staring at him.

She didn't wait to be told. She hurried toward the pilot and unbuckled his belt, showing surprising strength as she helped ease him to the floor.

"What's wrong with him?" she asked, beginning the first maneuvers of CPR.

Dan gave her a nod of approval as he slipped into the pilot's seat and assumed control of the plane. "I don't know," he said. "He was fine this morning." He checked the instrument panel. They had lost critical altitude. He set the plane to climb back into the sky.

Celeste felt Kip's neck. "He doesn't seem to be in severe distress. His pulse is regular and steady."

Dan made an adjustment in the plane and then turned his attention to Celeste and the pilot. Out of the corner of his eye he noticed that the black cat had joined them.

"He's breathing okay," Dan observed.

"It's like he's asleep," Celeste said, rocking back on her heels.

"Or like he's been drugged."

"Meow!" The black cat came into the cockpit. He seemed to examine the pilot and then went to the console where the remains of a cup of coffee were in a holder. He batted the cup with his paw. "Meow!"

Celeste reached for the cup. She lifted it to her nose and inhaled. "It smells like coffee." She offered it to Dan.

He sniffed it and shook his head. "I can't tell."

"Meow!" the cat insisted.

Dan placed the cup back in the holder. "It's safe right there for now, and when we land, I'll see about sending it to the lab to get it tested."

"You think someone drugged your pilot?" Celeste got a pillow from storage and put it under Kip's head.

"I hope that's all it is," Dan said grimly. "Kip will recover from a sleeping pill."

"Who would do this?" Celeste asked.

Dan registered the panic in her voice. He forced his own reply to be calm. "Offhand, I wouldn't care to comment. But I promise you that I'll get to the bottom of this. We all could have been killed."

Celeste nodded. He could see that she was biting her bottom lip. "What is it?" he asked.

"What if this is about me?" she whispered, unable to meet his gaze. "You know I'm on the run."

"You mean you think your husband might try to wreck a plane?" Dan was incredulous. He'd never assumed that Celeste had anything to do with the chain of events. He'd immediately thought it was connected to his latest business venture. But she *had* been physically assaulted.

"We could have been followed last night when you took me home. People know who you are. They could have put two and two together. Maybe they only meant to delay the flight. I can't believe they'd risk innocent lives." She dropped her head lower. "Then again, I can't underestimate certain factions of my...people," Celeste said slowly. Her rich voice was dull and flat and her eyes showed a loss of hope. "They're capable of anything," she said clearly.

Chapter Four

Celeste held Kip's head as he sipped the water she offered. She was aware of Dan's glances at her, but she focused instead on the pilot, who was improving with each passing minute. Kip shifted and she settled his head onto her lap. "It's okay," she said, reassuring him as he blinked up at her. "Everything is fine." He closed his eyes and seemed to doze.

Dan's voice, so close, was like a touch. "Where did you learn your bedside manner?" he asked. "You're the first businesswoman I've met who could pass herself off as Florence Nightingale."

"Caring for the sick and elderly is a part of life for everyone," Celeste answered. "At least in my community."

"Where were you raised?" Dan asked with a chuckle. "It sounds like a pretty unusual place."

All her life she'd viewed herself as apart, as different. Her people, the Roma, chose to remain isolated from mainstream American life. But never had she been so aware of the reasons why.

For centuries her people had been wanderers, travelers with skills and talents sought by the people whose villages they passed through. Their life had revolved around family and their individual clans, or *vistas,* and the greater organization of the Romany people. Part of the isolation was self-imposed, but another part was that, as wanderers, Gypsies had been accused of every crime, every theft that happened. So they had learned to rely on only themselves. The bond between them had become so close and tight that they became a nation on the move. Some immigrated to America, and one branch, her branch, had finally settled in Texas. Rulers had been chosen, laws set into place. And she had broken those rules. Now, she was an outcast. She closed her eyes for a second, overwhelmed at the consequences of her actions.

"Celeste? Is something wrong?"

Dan's concerned voice brought her back to the moment. There was plenty wrong, but she could tell him of none of it. "Who would do this?" she asked, afraid that she knew the answer. She had been a fool to think she could walk away from her family, from her people and her obligations. Her hand went to her chest where the ring of her people dangled on a chain beneath her shirt. She was the only child of Ramone Levert. Her husband would rule the large settlement of Gypsies that had called Texas their home for the past thirty years.

"We'll find out." He put a hand on her shoulder and gave it a gentle squeeze. "Don't worry. Once we land, it won't seem so frightening."

The pilot grimaced and opened his eyes. His focus took in Celeste as she bent over him and then Dan in the pilot's seat. Celeste gave silent thanks that Kip seemed to be coming around without signs of permanent injury.

"What happened?" Kip asked in a slurred voice.

"We'll find out as soon as we land," Dan answered. "Which should be in about fifteen minutes." He smiled at the pilot, who sat up and shook his head like a dog. "Good thing you taught me to fly this baby."

Kip nodded. "Damn good thing." He started to rise, and Celeste gave him support. Together they headed back to the passenger section where Kip dropped into a seat. "My head is about to explode."

"Dan's radioed the airport and paramedics will meet the plane." Celeste took note that Kip's color was better, and his respiration had leveled out, but there was intense pain in his eyes. "They'll take care of you," she reassured him. As if to reaffirm her words, the black cat hopped into the seat beside Kip and curled up, ready for a nap. Celeste reached over and stroked his sleek fur, taking comfort in the feel of him.

Kip rubbed his face. "I can't figure out what happened. I was fine, and then I got groggy. And then…"

"Did anyone have access to the plane?" Celeste asked.

Kip thought a moment. "I suppose anyone who had clearance at the airport could have gotten aboard. I got everything ready for an early takeoff, and then I went into the city."

"So, there was no one on the plane last night?" Celeste asked.

"There shouldn't have been. Someone could have boarded her, I suppose. It doesn't seem likely, but it could happen."

Celeste patted his shoulder. "We'll figure it out later." She felt her own anxiety intensify. Her father would not have done something so terrible. No matter how angry he was at her, he would never hurt her, or endanger others. But Trell Sylvest was another matter. Celeste didn't trust him, and she had gravely insulted him by running away from the marriage. Perhaps one of his men had somehow overheard the conversation in the maze the night before. He might have intended to drug the pilot and delay the takeoff. Even at his worst, she'd never thought Trell capable of murder. And what would he gain by killing her? None of it made sense. But someone had drugged the pilot. That couldn't be denied. Perhaps the drugs had been intended for her or Dan. There was no way to tell. But she owed it to Dan to tell him the truth. And there was no time like the present. Whatever the consequences, she couldn't remain silent any longer.

"Excuse me," she said, rising. "I need to speak to Mr. Carson. Will you be okay?"

"Certainly," Kip said, putting his head back and closing his eyes. "I'm feeling more like myself all the time. When I find out who's responsible for this, I pity them."

Celeste walked the short distance to the cockpit and stood for a moment watching Dan at the controls. His hands moved over the delicate panel, making small adjustments to the plane. His head turned left and right, intent on his work. The plane responded to his slightest touch, and Celeste was shocked at the thought that she, too, would react to his slightest whisper, his gentlest touch. The sensation of desire was so strong, so unbidden, that her body trembled.

She put a hand out to steady herself against the door frame and watched the sunlight in his longish, gently curled blond hair. He was not like the men she'd grown up knowing. Maybe the difference was only physical. Her people were dark-haired with olive skin. Handsome, to be sure. But Dan's sheer blondness was captivating. She must be fascinated by his looks, nothing more. And she could control her reaction.

She reminded herself that she knew nothing about him—and that was the way it was going to remain. He was a kind man, a generous man to offer her help and a job. Whatever strange feelings he evoked in her she would have to govern and suppress. She had never been the kind of woman who became infatuated with a man, and she wasn't about to become one.

He sensed her presence and turned around. "Celeste, is Kip okay?"

"I think so. He seems to be getting stronger. And angrier," she added. "The cat was right. It was the coffee, wasn't it?" It wasn't the most direct way to tell him what she had to, but it was a beginning.

"Yes, I think so." His face drew into a frown. "I'm sorry you've gotten caught up in this. I don't want you to think that Carson Dynamics is a dangerous place to work. It's just that I've become involved in a business deal that's highly competitive."

She could tell he was choosing his words carefully. But the amazing thing was that he thought the incident was directed at him. "Mr. Carson, I—"

"I know this has unsettled you, but once you're in Houston, you won't be involved in this end of the business. We need someone to work as an analyst, and you won't have anything to do with the more speculative part of our investing."

"It isn't that. I have to tell you—"

"Just give it a chance. Naturally, if you don't like the job, you're free to go and I'll see about helping you find a position with another company. I can't tell you how sorry I am about all of this.'' He finally turned to look at her and Celeste was stopped by the sincerity of his gaze.

The easiest thing would be to give in. To smile and accept his generosity. She was out of the reach of her family, and Trell, at least for a little while. Houston would be a good city to start over in. She should just keep her mouth shut and go on. But she couldn't. "What if all of this is my fault?"

Dan nodded slowly. "I've thought about that, and I think it's impossible." His smile was rueful. "I find it interesting that both of us have people chasing us. It gives us something in common, doesn't it?"

Celeste couldn't resist his smile. Her own was tentative. "Not exactly what I'd like to have in common with anyone."

"Truer words were never spoken." Dan motioned her to take the copilot's seat. "We're about to land," he said. "Look, you'll be fine in Houston. Now, buckle up and say good morning to my town."

DAN HELPED KIP into the ambulance, closing the door on the grumbling pilot who insisted he didn't need medical attention. Dan ignored him and firmly shut the door. Although Kip appeared to have recovered, Dan was taking no chances. Kip was a longtime friend as well as an employee. If there were any repercussions from the incident, Dan wanted to know. He retrieved the container of coffee, the pot that Kip had brewed and the beans that had been ground, as well as the filters and coffeepot. He would have it all tested.

Although his mind was on the details, he was also

aware of the woman who waited beside the limo. Celeste Sanchez wore a worried frown and carried a heart full of troubles. Even a one-eyed fool could see that much. He sighed. She sincerely believed that her ex-husband might have attempted to kill her by bringing down a plane with two other passengers. Now, that was something to cause concern. As Dan started toward the limo and Celeste, he put a smile on his face. What horrors had she endured in a marriage if she thought her husband capable of murder?

He was watching her intently, and he saw the way she looked up at his approach, like a wild animal startled by a hunter. The pain that struck him was so sudden, so visceral that he stumbled. Celeste Sanchez was vulnerable and alone. And potentially very dangerous, he reminded himself. The one thing he couldn't afford was feelings for this woman. He didn't need another lesson in guilt and suffering, and Celeste Sanchez had enough problems of her own without taking on the curse of the Carsons.

"Dan!" The familiar voice shouted to him over the noise of the airport, and he turned to greet his mother with a smile. Diana Carson waved to him from the open door of her car. She stood up as he changed directions and went toward her. He gave her a hug and a kiss on the cheek. "You didn't need to come to the airport."

"I got the message that you'd had some trouble with the plane." She glanced at the small jet and then back at her son. "Kip was injured?"

"We're not certain." Dan stepped back from his mother. She was a partner in Carson Dynamics, and there were things he needed to tell her. But not here or now. "We'll discuss it later." He saw her gaze shift to Celeste.

"Who is that?"

Dan smiled. "A young woman with luck almost as good as mine."

"Dan?" Diana's face registered worry.

"Don't even think about it," he assured her. "She was in trouble and I gave her a hand. She's going to work for us as an analyst. There's nothing else there."

Diana's brown eyes lifted and she stared into her son's face. "I wish—"

"I do, too, Mother. But I'm not willing to risk another woman's life or my heart in an experiment to see if the curse really exists. Shawna was enough for me, enough pain for a lifetime."

He felt her hand on his arm. "Accidents *do* happen, Daniel."

Dan forced his mind past Shawna and thought of his sister and brother. "Tell it to Angie, who was left at the altar. Or Greg, who saw his fiancée marry his best friend. No, I think I have enough evidence to believe that love is the most dangerous weapon in the hands of a Carson."

"But your father and I were deeply in love," Diana insisted. "It's so unfair that some foolish woman's curse could deny my children such a necessary part of life. There are times when I think we must all be mad to even consider such a thing...."

Dan put his arm around his mother's shoulders. "Remember, none of us believed it. I still didn't believe it after my sister's suffering, or my brother's pain. It wasn't until my bride was killed on the way to our wedding that I became a believer. And trust me, now I believe."

Diana sighed, nodding at Celeste. "Well, whatever else your protégée may be, she's a beautiful young woman. And is that a cat with her?"

"A stray that helped her out in a pinch." When he saw his mother's skeptical look, he laughed. "It's true. The cat came to her rescue, and then there was this black panther—"

"You always did have the wildest imagination," Diana said, lightly slapping his arm. "A black cat *and* a dark beauty. Very intriguing."

"Now, there I can agree with you," Dan said. "Let me introduce you. She's obviously aware that we're talking about her, and I'm afraid she's had rather a bad twenty-four hours."

Dan led his mother across the short stretch of tarmac and made the introductions. "Celeste was working at Stevens and Lynch when I stole her away."

"An excellent company," Diana said, taking Celeste's hand and giving it a squeeze. "Welcome to Carson Dynamics. My son has an innate ability to find the brightest and most talented of employees."

"Mother heads the investment side of the business," Dan explained to Celeste. "You'll be working for her."

"And it's lucky you are that you don't work for that tyrant," Diana said, smiling at her son. "He's never home, always gallivanting around the world putting deals together."

Dan could see that Celeste's anxiety had been lessened by his mother's friendly words, and he hoped he'd done the right thing by bringing her to Houston.

"Mother, I thought Celeste could use the suite we keep at The Admiralty until she finds a place to live."

"And the cat?" Celeste asked.

"No problem," Diana assured her, bending down to stroke the cat's back. "We're all animal lovers in the Carson family. In fact, my dog Pookie goes to work with me." She lifted the cat into her arms. "Why he's as black as a witch's familiar."

"Meow!" Familiar nuzzled under her chin.

"What's his name?" Diana asked.

"Well, I haven't named him." Celeste reached out and tickled his chin. "But he seemed to like Familiar."

"Meow!" the cat nodded. "Meow!"

Celeste laughed softly. "I think he's picked his own name. Familiar it is."

Dan watched the concern peel away from Celeste. It was one of the things he loved best about his mother. She had a kind heart, and she always made others feel welcome and wanted. Even stray women with stray cats.

"Then it's settled. Familiar is his name," he said, putting a hand on each woman's shoulder. "Now, you two head for The Admiralty where Celeste and Familiar can get settled, and I have an errand to run."

"There is such a thing as an office and work," Diana said archly.

"I'll be at the office," Dan promised her. "But I need to take care of one small detail." He saw the worry return to Celeste's face and he knew she was aware of his errand. He was taking the coffee to a lab for testing.

"Don't worry," he said, kissing his mother's cheek. "You'll get your share of work out of me before the day is over."

Before any further objections could be raised, he headed toward the car that waited for him. He could only hope that Celeste wouldn't talk about the possibility of Kip having been drugged until he had more facts.

CELESTE SETTLED into the luxurious car with Familiar on her lap. She hadn't expected Dan's mother. As she glanced at Diana Carson, a petite woman with dark, gray-threaded hair and intense brown eyes, Celeste missed her own mother. Maria Levert was the antithesis of Diana Carson. Maria was plump and had never worn a business suit or high heels. But the two women had one thing in common—they loved their children. Diana's love for Dan was so obvious that Celeste could almost taste it. Yet there was an openness between the two that Celeste had never experienced with her mother. Diana had truly allowed her son to grow up. They were mother and son, indeed, but they were also individuals who chose to love each other. Celeste knew that she and Maria were a long way from such a mature relationship.

"Where are you from, Celeste?" Diana asked.

Celeste hesitated only a few seconds. "Lomar, a small town not far from Dallas."

Diana turned to look fully at her. "Lomar?"

"Yes," Celeste spoke with slight hesitation. "Do you know it?"

Diana seemed to recover herself. "No, not really. I knew someone who lived there once."

"Who?" Celeste felt her stomach tighten. Lomar was a fairly close-knit community.

Diana's smile was forced. "It was a long time ago. It doesn't matter, and she's probably long gone." She glanced out the window. "She wanted to leave the area. I'm sure she followed her dream and went to New York."

Celeste didn't press the issue. She'd told Dan only half the truth, and she didn't want to start a string of lies with Diana Carson, the woman who would be her boss.

"Have you always lived in Houston?" Celeste asked, hoping to turn the focus of the conversation onto her host.

"No, I grew up around Dallas, but when my husband and I started Carson Dynamics, we needed to be closer to the oil industry. Houston was the logical choice."

"Tell me about the company," Celeste said, relaxing back into her seat. The purring cat on her lap gave her a great deal of comfort, and she was amused by the way he seemed to follow the conversation.

"We've mostly focused on wild-catting operations here in the United States. As the company grew, I began to develop the investment side of Carson Dynamics. Now we're balanced between aggressive investing in oil and the marketplace." She smiled. "I never viewed myself as a risk taker until I met Jake. And then it was Katy-bar-the-door. He brought out the gambler in me."

Celeste knew without asking that Jake Carson was no longer alive. It was in the way Diana spoke of him, and the hint of sadness that seemed to be in her eyes. "Your son seems to enjoy a gamble, too."

Diana laughed. "Dan is worse than Jake or me. He loves a gamble. The higher the stakes, the better." Diana's face turned troubled. "Except where his heart is concerned."

Celeste forced a smile, but a sudden chill touched

her. More than anything, she needed to play it safe. Risk taking was something she couldn't afford. "I'm afraid I might not be cut out for your company," she said. "I'm more conservative."

Diana put a hand on her arm. "Don't worry about that. You'll balance out our wilder impulses." She gave Celeste an assessing look. "If you climbed into a plane with a man you didn't know, you're not a coward. You must have had plenty of reason to leave Dallas. I'm not asking now, but remember that I'm available to talk if you ever need me. And take this advice. Give yourself a chance at Carson Dynamics. If it doesn't work out, both Dan and I will help you find another job."

Celeste felt the tears spring to her eyes. Why were these people being so good to her? She'd always been told that only her own family would protect and help her. But that wasn't true. These strangers had rushed to her defense. "Thank you," she said.

"Look, there's The Admiralty." Diana pointed toward a majestic old hotel.

"It's lovely," Celeste said. "It has the air of a fairy-tale castle."

"The staff is excellent, and you can stay as long as you wish. We keep several suites here for visitors. In fact, I think Dan will also be staying here." She smiled. "I'm going to let you out and head back to the office. Why don't you take the rest of the day to settle in, pick up some maps and get an idea of the layout of the city? I'll send the car for you tomorrow at nine."

"That would be wonderful. I do feel like I've been caught up in a tornado." The limo stopped at the front of the hotel and a liveried doorman stepped up to open her door.

"You'll be fine. And if they give you any guff about the cat, tell them to call me."

Celeste held Familiar in her arms. "We're going to be perfectly fine."

THIS TIME I think I may have leaped before I looked. Speaking of leaping, I think I need to abandon Celeste's tender arms and scope out this hotel. It does indeed have the look of a fairy-tale castle, but as I recall, eating and drinking in fairy tales tend to lead to spells, charms and hundred-year comas. I want to make sure the kitchen here is stocked up on kitty delicacies. After all, I left that big Sweetheart bash to defend the mysterious goddess, and I haven't had much of a meal since then. I mean, tuna was okay, but now I'm ready for a real meal.

Don't panic, Gorgeous Goddess, I'll be back in one shake of a rat's tail. But I need to examine the premises. I'll just duck around this tree, cut through this beautiful little garden and voilà! I've managed to escape. I can tell Celeste is upset by my defection, but it will only gladden her heart when I make my way up to the suite. Right now, I have serious PI business to attend to.

While GG and Mrs. Carson were talking, I noticed a car was following us. Perhaps it's my imagination, but I think not. Black sedan. I mean really, don't villains ever get tired of black? Wouldn't navy or gray do just as well? And isn't black awfully hot down here in Texas? Let me saunter over and see if this guy is clever enough to also be wearing a black hat.

Uh-oh, he's watching me. Smarter than your av-

*erage human. Now he's putting on his dark glasses.
And he's rolling down the window. What an unhappy
face!*

"Beat it, cat!"

*Not as smart as I thought. He tried to scat me.
Imagine. And he's staring a hole in Celeste. But he's
also watching the Carson limousine. So, is he watching Diana or Celeste? The limo is pulling away and
he's staying, so it must be the Goddess he's after.*

*Yes, he's getting out and signaling the valet. He's
going into the hotel. Now's my chance to prove my
value as Familiar, the best detective in the world.
Well, perhaps that isn't accurate. The best detective
in the universe. Yes, that's more in line with the truth.*

Chapter Five

Dan paced the sterile white corridor of the lab and gritted his teeth. He'd already called the hospital. Kip had been thoroughly checked over and released. There were traces of a barbiturate in his bloodstream, but there had been no permanent damage.

A door opened and a tall man with glasses came toward Dan. He held a clipboard in his hand and when he stopped in front of Dan he flipped two pages before he spoke. "The coffee beans had apparently been soaked in somadreen, a very potent sedative," the man said. "There was enough sedative in the beans to put a football team to sleep. Luckily he only drank a cup."

"Thanks," Dan said. It was the information he needed. There was still no way to tell who the drug was intended for. But he'd already put some of his men to work at the Dallas/Ft. Worth airport. Once he found the target, it would be easier to find the culprit.

"Although somadreen is a potent drug, it isn't normally used in lethal doses," the chemist said carefully. "I understand the pilot of your plane was drugged?"

"That's right."

"In a situation such as that, somadreen could be a deadly drug. Mr. Carson, I hope you take this seriously. I'm not a policeman, but it seems to me that someone is trying to kill you."

"I'll keep that in mind," Dan said. "Thanks for your time and talent. Send the bill to my office."

"Will do," the chemist said as he watched Dan walk away.

Dan left Southwest Laboratories and headed for the office. He'd traded the company limo for his own sports car, and he pressed the accelerator as he pulled onto the interstate. The fine-tuned response of the car made him relax and for a few moments he concentrated on his driving.

He went over what he knew about Celeste Sanchez. She was fleeing an abusive husband. And she'd hinted that perhaps her family had tried to kill her and everyone else aboard the plane. That was a heavy-duty accusation.

Dan didn't believe Celeste or her husband was at the bottom of the drugging incident, but what he was left thinking made him extremely uncomfortable. The only person who'd known about his plans was his old roommate, Jess Harper.

He mentioned specifically at the ball that he would be leaving early the next morning to fly to Houston. And Jess was the only person he'd told. Which meant that if it wasn't someone associated with Celeste, then it had to be Jess.

Jess also knew enough about Dan and his plane to be able to talk his way around airport authorities.

Dan's fists clenched on the steering wheel. He hadn't wanted to believe Rick Hanson when the CIA agent said that Jess had stepped over the line between right and wrong once too often. Jess had always been the Friday night party boy, the young turk who loved the nightlife and the fast lane. But he'd always had a good foundation. He was a man who loved to gamble, but he'd never risked too much or gotten in so deep over his head that he'd abandoned his principles.

But Dan had to concede that he'd been away from Dallas and his old friend for a long, long time. And Dan knew he, personally, had changed. Why was it so impossible to believe that Jess had changed, too?

Jess had agreed to set up the meeting with Dan and the two oil investors. He hadn't bothered to say he didn't know the men. He'd listened to the deal that Dan had presented, just as Rick Hanson had plotted it out, and then agreed to it. Seemingly without a qualm.

Dan shook his head slowly. It still almost broke his heart. Even though his eyes were on the thick Houston traffic, his mind went back to an old memory. It was the night of the spring dance sponsored each year by Dallas businesses for the university students. It was a chance for college students to mingle with prospective employers, to sample the good life of the corporate CEO that some of the graduates would soon achieve. And Dan and Jess had been there, hot tickets for the company presidents who casually made small talk with prospective employees.

They had been convinced of their invincibility. Dan remembered the two of them, dressed to the nines. Shawna Wright on his arm, the most beautiful woman in the room. And the smartest. Mr. Brando, the head of First Texas Banks and one of the business school professors, had come over to them. He'd looked at Dan and nodded at Jess before he spoke. "I'd thought

I'd offer one of you two gentlemen the best job in the state, but I've already selected the college student to fill it,'' he'd said.

"And who would that be?" Dan had asked, exchanging surprised looks with Jess. Both of them had anticipated the job offer.

"The woman standing beside you," Brando had answered, laughing at the look on Dan's face. "She's just as smart, just as talented and not nearly so cocky," he'd said, laughing as he lifted his drink. "To an excellent crop of business students," he'd said in an impromptu toast.

A car horn blared and Dan pulled his attention back to his driving, surprised to discover that the memory had left him shaken.

He tried hard not to think about Shawna, and usually he was more successful. It was not the pain of her loss that tormented him, but the guilt he felt. Had he not asked her to marry him, she would be alive. He'd been so cocky and self-assured that even after the tragic events of his brother's and sister's romantic lives, he'd been sure the curse had somehow excluded him. That he was smart enough to avoid it.

And Shawna Wright was dead.

The high-rise profile of Carson Dynamics filled the windshield as he turned right, and Dan pulled into his parking spot. It really was good to be home. He loved his work. It was the one place he could forget the past, forget Shawna and all the things he would never have.

His pleasure was short-lived as he recognized the man standing in the shadow of a side entrance of the building. What was Rick Hanson doing in Houston?

When Dan had spoken with him the night before, Hanson had been in Washington.

As Dan got out of the car, Rick stepped forward. "I heard you had a little trouble on the flight."

Dan wanted to brush past him. Hanson was little better than the crooks he was paid to apprehend. But he did carry a federal badge and the weight of his office. "What are you doing in Houston?"

"Curiosity. I've always wanted to see Houston. And I had some information for you about Ms. Sanchez. I wanted to deliver it personally."

Something in Rick's tone alerted Dan. "What?"

"As far as we can discover, Celeste Sanchez doesn't exist. There's no social security number for her, no birth certificate, no immigration papers." He shrugged. "Your new friend has an assumed identity."

Dan wasn't completely shocked. Celeste had told him she was on the run. She would be foolish if she was still using her husband's name. "This was information that had to be delivered in person?" Rick's eager face annoyed him.

"I thought I'd take a look at her myself. I suppose it didn't occur to you that she may be a plant."

Dan's eyes narrowed, but it was the only reaction he allowed. It had not occurred to him that Celeste Sanchez might be on Phil Norris's payroll. From the first time his eyes met hers, he'd failed to consider anything about her except what she chose to tell him. He felt anger building, but it was at himself.

"Do you have evidence that she's working for Norris?" Dan snapped.

Rick held up a hand. "Hold on a minute. I didn't say she was. I said it was a possibility. I mean, you offer her a ride on your jet and suddenly your pilot is drugged." He arched one eyebrow. "Think about it."

"What, exactly, did you find out about Celeste Sanchez?" Dan kept his temper carefully in check. Rick enjoyed needling him, and he wouldn't give him the satisfaction of seeing that he'd scored.

"She doesn't exist." Rick shrugged and pulled a camera out of his pocket. "I thought I'd get some photos and check them against some of the women in the files. Women known to work in this type of business."

At the thought of Celeste as some type of international spy, Dan felt amusement because it was so ridiculous. Unless, of course, she was very, very good at it. She projected an innocence that was dated in this day and age. And Dan would be willing to bet a lot that it wasn't an act. "She's at The Admiralty," Dan said. "I think you're running a rabbit trail. She's a woman who's trying to escape an abusive husband. She's not a spy or someone working for international oil smugglers."

Rick put the camera in his pocket. "I hope you're right, Dan. Because once you make one bad decision, you have to second-guess yourself all the time."

Dan stepped closer to the CIA agent. "I don't know what your game is, Hanson. You take a lot of pleasure in needling me. Now, I'm not really happy about this plan you've cooked up, but I agreed to help you because I felt it was the right thing to do for my country. Keep it up, though, and you can find someone else to play bait for your trap." Dan brusquely turned away and headed toward the front door.

"Don't kid yourself, Carson. You're helping because you didn't have a. choice,'' Rick called after him.

Dan took the steps and entered the front of the building without turning back. If he did turn around, he knew the insolent look on Rick Hanson's face would force him to do something he'd regret.

CELESTE PICKED UP the telephone for the fifth time, only to replace it and return to pacing the room.

"Meow." Familiar jumped on the bedside table and swatted the receiver with his paw. "Meow."

"So, you think I should call?" Celeste asked, so relieved at having a concurring opinion that she didn't question that it came from a cat.

"Meow." Familiar pushed several buttons and Celeste heard the operator asking for the number that she wished to call.

She cast a long look at the cat as she picked up the receiver and gave the number. It was midmorning, and chances were that her mother was alone in the house. Celeste simply couldn't continue without letting Maria know she was safe.

The phone rang three times before there was an answer, and Celeste recognized the voice of Anna, their longtime housekeeper.

"Anna, it's me, Celeste. I want to speak with Mother."

"Celeste!" There was such relief in the older woman's voice that Celeste felt the tear spring to her eyes. "We've been worried sick. Your mother has not eaten. Your father has not come home."

"I'm sorry," Celeste said, forcing herself not to completely cave under the guilt she felt. "Let me talk to Mother."

"Mrs. Levert! Mrs. Levert!"

Celeste took a deep breath and waited until she heard her mother's excited voice on the end of the line.

"I'm fine, Mother," she reassured Maria. "I'm safe."

"Celeste, your father was furious at first, but now he's only worried. Please come home. He will forgive you."

Celeste gripped the phone tighter. "Has he given up the idea of my marriage to Trell?"

There was a pause. "Your father didn't arrange the marriage as a way to punish you or make you unhappy. He selected a man who would make you a good husband. The way Ramone was chosen for me. If you would only come home, you would see that this is the best way. You are heir to the Levert name, Celeste. You are the child of Ramone Levert. You have position and responsibility."

"I have a right to be happy," Celeste said softly. Why had she even thought it would be different? There was one thing she knew about her father. Ramone Levert never backed down from a decision. It was one of the reasons he was the best leader her people had ever had. It was also the reason his only child was now on the run.

"Celeste, when I was your age, I thought I knew best. I ran away from home, too." Maria Levert's voice took on a soft edge. "I met a man and fell in love with him. He was so handsome. So tall and blond with blue eyes that seemed to see all of life so clearly."

Celeste felt a twinge of dread. Her mother had never talked of this. Maria Levert was a woman of great pride. As the wife of the ruler, much of her life was public display. What parts were private, Maria guarded closely. And she had never spoken of her youth. Especially not of a time when she disobeyed the laws of her people. In an attempt to bring Celeste home, Maria was revealing a secret part of herself. She had abandoned her normal reserve, and Celeste knew how much this was costing her.

"What happened to you isn't going to happen to me," Celeste said as calmly as she could. "I'm not in love with anyone. I have a good job and a safe place to be. That's all I wanted to tell you. I'm safe, Mother. I have a chance to be happy. I just want to be left alone to live my life."

"That's not possible, Celeste. Listen to me. I thought I knew best, and the end result was heartbreak. You think you can step out into the world, away from your people, but you'll discover that you can't. You've been raised to assume a certain position. You have a duty and a heritage that you can't turn your back on, no matter how you try."

"I'm not refusing my duty, Mother, but I am refusing to marry a man I don't like. A man I don't respect. That I can refuse."

Maria ignored her. "When I came back to the family, I married Ramone, as my father had planned for me. It was the best thing for me. Your father and I have been very happy. I promise you, if you come home, you'll find the happiness you seek."

Celeste brushed a tear from her cheek. She'd never heard her mother sound so vulnerable. But there was not a trace of a change in her attitude toward the marriage. Celeste had hoped that by leaving she would prove to her family that she would never submit to Trell Sylvest as her husband. Apparently, her feelings still didn't matter.

"Mother, know that I'm safe. Please tell Father to quit looking for me. Even if you find me, I won't marry Trell. Tell him that." Her voice broke. "And tell him that I love him. I love you both." She hung up the phone before she began to cry.

WELL ME, oh, my. I should probably feel guilty about listening in on the extension in the bathroom, but sometimes the end justifies the means, at least when I'm involved. It seems I've fallen in with the Princess of the Gypsies. I recognized her royal bearing, and her beauty. But I had no idea. I'm a little flabbergasted. My idea of Gypsies needs a little updating— I suppose violins and campfires and dancing with those cute, brightly painted wagons all circled around a campfire is a little too Hollywood. But I had no idea there were real Gypsies in Texas.

But all speculating aside, it pains me to see Celeste so upset. It's plain to me that her family has arranged a marriage for her. Rather archaic, but throughout history, marriage has always been viewed by royalty as a business venture more than a romantic coupling.

But Celeste finds her chosen husband to be seriously objectionable. Trell. It's not a name I've ever heard, but I already don't like him. What kind of man would agree to marry a woman who didn't want him? One who's looking at her title more than her heart.

The problem I see here is that her family can easily trace that call, if her mother wants to. I encouraged her to reach out and touch someone, but I didn't realize she was heir to a royal title at the time. Now there's a chance her family will send someone to try to bring her home. I suppose this means that one black cat is on guard duty.

I am relieved about one thing. Celeste wasn't involved in the plane fiasco. If her family wants her to marry someone, they wouldn't try to kill her in a plane crash. No, there's something else going on here.

My job at the moment is to purr a little and give Celeste some comfort, and then do a little exploring. This is a great old hotel with plenty of hidey-holes. That's going to make it a lot easier to slip around.

I want to take a look at the room Dan is staying in. There's something not right here. And I also need to use a telephone. I'm sure Ashley and Brak are frantic by now.

You know, it's not that I don't care about the worry I cause, but a detective can't be hamstrung by too much tenderness. I remember back in my first days with Eleanor. She worried every time I went out the front door. I'd go over for a visit with Clotilde, and Eleanor would be out with a flashlight calling all over the neighborhood.

Yeah, she loves me.

Humans aren't so different. I know Celeste's mother is worried about her. It's that old tug between freedom and safety. Well, Celeste is in good hands. Or should I say paws. As long as I'm around, nothing bad is going to happen to her.

Now watch a master cat at work. I'll just slide up into her lap and soak up a few of those tears in my black coat. There she goes, petting and stroking, and just as I thought, her crying is beginning to slow down. That's it, Celeste, take a few deep breaths and collect yourself. Take a nice little nap. That's a good girl. And now for the window.

I love these hotels with balconies. This is sort of a turret style. Very classic. It makes life exciting for a cat with great balance.

Chapter Six

Dan entered the seven-story office building of glass and chrome and was immediately greeted with a warm hello from Helen, the receptionist at the front desk.

"Welcome back, Mr. Carson."

"Thank you," he said, smiling at the young woman's enthusiasm and energy. It was good to be home. All around him Carson Dynamics seemed to hum. After his father's death, Dan and his mother had reluctantly taken up the reins of the family business. They'd divided the duties, each taking those best suited to his or her talents. And during the past seven years, they'd gathered around them the brightest employees. As Dan strode through the first-floor lobby to the bank of elevators, he felt the vibrancy of the business. He had created a place where hard work and effort was rewarded—and it showed in the faces of the employees.

Basically, Carson Dynamics put together money for business deals. Oil had always been a staple of the deals Dan invested in, but until last year, Carson Dynamics had exclusively bought domestic oil. The decision to shift to a more global market had actually been his mother's, and one she'd made without consulting him. The venture into foreign oil was now the problem that had brought Rick Hanson into his life.

Three months before, Diana had met with several oil brokers who claimed to have access to oil from Saudi Arabia. The deal required an instant decision, and his mother had approved the buy. Carson Dynamics was already in too deep when Dan had discovered they were importing oil that the U.S. had embargoed. It had been an honest mistake, but one that Rick Hanson had quickly capitalized on.

And when the CIA came questioning the deal, Dan had assumed the burden of the mistake. Diana's name was never mentioned, and he had no intention of telling his mother where her actions had led the company.

Rick readily agreed that Carson Dynamics had innocently made a mistake, but nonetheless, the CIA agent was threatening to bring charges against Dan, his mother and the company unless Dan agreed to help in an international sting.

It was, essentially, blackmail. And that grated on Dan. But if he intended to protect his mother and the company, there was nothing he could do but play along.

The CIA agent had enlisted Dan to continue to do business with Phil Norris in an attempt to lure the two international brokers onto U.S. soil where they could be arrested. Dan had no problem in helping capture the two crooks—he believed in his country—but he did object to using innocent third parties such as Jess Harper.

But Dan couldn't be certain how innocent Jess actually was.

He entered the elevator and punched the button for the seventh floor. When the door opened, Betty greeted him with a cup of coffee and a sheaf of newspaper articles she'd clipped while he was away.

"Thanks," he said, taking the coffee and the folder. "I don't know how much I pay you, Betty, but it isn't enough."

"It's plenty, this week. But when the annual raises come due, we'll talk," she said, laughing. "Your mother wants to see you and there was a call from Jess Harper in Dallas. He said it was urgent."

Dan had started toward his mother's office but sidetracked to his own. He dialed Jess's number and eased down into the leather chair at his desk. He recognized his friend's voice as soon as he came on the line.

"Dan, I heard you had some trouble in the air," Jess said. "I couldn't get any details, but I wanted to make sure you were okay."

Or make sure I had crashed, Dan thought, and then instantly felt ashamed. Jess wasn't a murderer. "It wasn't much of anything. Kip got sick, but I took over the plane and everything was fine." Dan played it very casual.

"Is Kip okay?"

"He had some tests at the hospital, and they assure me he's perfectly fine. Just one of those sudden things. Something he ate." He concentrated on listening to Jess's tone. Jess knew Kip. The pilot had worked for the company for a decade and had sometimes flown Jess.

"Thank goodness."

"How did you hear about it?" Dan asked. He'd radioed the Houston airport authorities, not Dallas.

"You know how gossip flies. Everyone who has a

plane heard it first and then it got spread even to those of us who have to take commercial flights,'' Jess said, laughing. "There were several people who expressed concern for you. Even though you haven't done business in Dallas in a while, you're still well thought of.''

"That's good to know," Dan responded. It made sense that the gossip about his mishap in the plane would spread from the airport. So perhaps Jess was telling the truth.

"Regarding the deal—I can set things up for Monday," Jess said. There was a hint of nervousness in his voice. "How's that for you?"

"Fine." It couldn't be over too soon.

"I'll take care of things from here," Jess said. "Listen, I've got some irons in the fire so I'd better hurry off. I just wanted to make sure you were okay, and I wanted to thank you for giving me a chance to participate in this deal. I never would have figured you to be involved in this kind of business, but I have to tell you it couldn't have come at a better time for me. I'm in over my head, as you probably guessed. I've been a little worried about this, but when we were younger, I always followed your lead, and you always got me through."

"Jess, I can't make any guarantees on this one." Dan felt his jaw tighten.

"You're one of the smartest men I know. You wouldn't risk all of this without knowing the odds. And thanks again for thinking of me, Dan. I've missed you. I mean after Shawna and all, I understood why you left Dallas, but I've really missed you. Now I'd better run."

Dan had no opportunity to respond. The phone line

went dead in his hand. "Damn," he whispered. Jess had all but admitted that he'd joined this deal because of Dan. It seemed he was luring his old friend into troubled waters. Although Rick Hanson had pointed out that Jess wouldn't participate in a crooked deal unless he had crooked tendencies, Dan wasn't so sure. Jess had often relied on his judgment in the past. Perhaps it wasn't the best business attribute—to let a friend be moral compass and risk guide—but it also wasn't a crime.

Dan picked up the phone and started to punch in Jess's number. It would be better if he warned Jess off this deal. He would word it so that he didn't give anything away, and Rick Hanson could find someone else to play middleman in the sting.

A light tap on his door signaled his mother's approach. He replaced the phone and opened the folder of newspaper clippings and pretended to be reviewing the stories Betty had collected on investments as his mother came in.

"Well, Dan, I thought you went to Dallas to do business. I didn't realize you were shopping for employees."

He could hear the teasing note in her voice, and he looked up with a grin. "I went for business and came back with a woman and a black cat. Now, I can't exactly recall how the cat figured into the plan."

"I wasn't aware you were scouting for investment talent."

"Celeste was just an unexpected bonus." Though Diana's tone was light, he could see the worry in her eyes. It was an irony, he thought, that Diana Carson was a woman who longed for grandchildren. She volunteered time at one of the Houston orphanages, a fact she tried to keep well hidden from her own children. And she sincerely believed that she would never have grandchildren of her own because of a stupid curse.

"She's a lovely young woman," Diana said, taking a seat with her own cup of coffee in hand. "She seems very sad."

"I think it's hard for her to leave her old life behind." He shut the file and focused his attention on his mother. "She'll be okay once she gets started in a job and finds a place of her own."

"Will you be okay?"

Diana's question startled him. "Of course. I'm not involved with her. I'm only helping her out."

Diana stared at him. "Something is troubling you, Dan. I know you. Whatever it is, you can tell me." Her gaze was assessing.

Dan held back the sigh and simply nodded his head. It would be a relief to tell his partner, but that was a luxury he couldn't afford. "Thanks, if something comes up, I'll be sure and let you know." He gave her a mischievous look. "It'll be just like being a kid again."

Rising from her chair, Diana crossed to his desk. "I couldn't help but notice that you've booked the plane for a trip to the ranch. On a Saturday evening?"

Dan met his mother's curious gaze. He'd hoped that she wouldn't notice, but he should have known better. Diana Carson was a terrific investor because she paid attention to the small details. Such as the plane.

"I thought the ranch would be quiet. I'm meeting some potential investors and I want to talk to them."

"Should I know about this?"

"Not yet. It's just an idea right now. When I have something more definite, I'll lay it all out on the table for you to evaluate."

"I haven't been to the ranch in a long time," Diana said.

The Carson ranch was a large spread north of San Antonio. Dan ran a herd of cattle on the thousand acres, but they were more for fun than profit. He'd chosen that location for the rendezvous with Jess and the international oil broker. He'd figured the ranch would be secluded and the best possible place for a showdown, if it came to that.

"It's business," he said easily.

"It might be a good change for me," Diana pressed.

This was what Dan had hoped to avoid. He didn't want his mother caught in a cross fire. "You know I respect your business acumen completely, but in this instance, it's a deal that requires a masculine touch."

Diana's eyebrows arched. "I thought such deals were out of date."

"They should be, but we both know they aren't. The men I'm meeting still believe that business is a man's world and women should be at home tending the hearth."

"Maybe I should show them a thing or two."

Dan's smile was forced. "It's a good opportunity for Carson Dynamics. These men may be old-fashioned, but we can make a lot of money." In the past seven years, he'd never put a business deal ahead of a matter of principle. But this time he couldn't risk having his mother on the premises. It was her feelings or her safety.

"I see," Diana said, and there was a coolness in her voice.

"I'm sorry. Maybe we can slowly bring them into the twentieth century. I'll work on them."

"Do whatever you think is best," she said. "I'm going over the investments we made in Tulsa. I should have a profit report ready this afternoon."

Dan's telephone rang and he nodded as Diana waved and left. He picked up the receiver, surprised to hear Kip's voice on the other end.

"I did some asking around about the plane," Kip said, his voice troubled. "There was someone at the Dallas airport early this morning poking around and asking questions. He claimed to be a friend of yours. The security at the airport wouldn't let him on the tarmac without your approval, but they think he knew your plane."

"What did he look like?" Dan asked.

"That's the problem. He wasn't memorable. Average height, dark hair, dark eyes, wearing an expensive suit. He could be a million people. He left a name," there was the sound of fumbling, "I wrote it down. Kenneth Martin."

Dan concentrated on the name. "It doesn't mean anything to me," he said. "What about you?"

"Nope. The odd thing is that this Martin had a badge. He said he was a Dallas cop."

This was surprising news. "Why would a cop be looking for me?"

"I checked with the city, and there isn't a Ken or Kenneth Martin on the payroll as a cop."

"So, he had a false badge?"

"Looks that way," Kip said. "Dan, this worries me. I know you've done some important business deals, and some of the people you do business with are extra cautious. But this isn't right. And if I'm not mistaken, there's someone watching me.''

''What do you mean?'' Dan knew the answer even as he asked, and he felt the tingle of warning at the base of his spine.

''I mean that there's a car parked outside my house with a guy sitting in it. It's been there since I got home. I'm on the verge of walking out the door and jerking the guy out of the vehicle and convincing him to tell me why he's following me around.''

''Don't go anywhere or do anything,'' Dan said. ''I'll take care of this.''

''How?''

But he didn't bother to answer. He replaced the phone and started out of his office. It was one thing for Rick Hanson to drag him into a dangerous mess, but now his employees were under surveillance. And in possible danger. Had the situation on the plane come down in a different way, Kip could have been killed.

This was not the bargain he'd cut with the CIA.

LET'S SEE HERE, the turret is pretty neat, and it isn't a long jump to the next window. Ahh, I made it with ease, and even a moderately competent human could probably do the same. So, now I'm in Dan's room.

And what I discover is that he's given the larger suite to our dark-eyed beauty. Now that's a gentleman. So far, Mr. Carson's manners have been impeccable. And they said chivalry was dead.

This investigation isn't going to take long at all. The drawers seem empty, the closet empty, nothing personal around here. Just Dan's bag, which one of the hotel employees brought up and unpacked for him. Not much to go on there except he uses a minty toothpaste and likes an expensive cologne and French cuffs on his dress shirt. Yes, indeed, a man with taste.

This has been a major waste of my investigative skills. So I'll see if I can't saunter into the main hotel. I need to find a place to relax and see if the watcher is still there. He gave me the slip earlier—not an easy thing to accomplish. But it was either follow him into the restaurant or make sure that GG made it to the room safely. And being a cat of refined taste, I stayed with the dame.

I think if I pull this silken cord beside the bed, it has the effect of immediate room service. Now, this is a classy touch. One or two sharp jerks and in a matter of moments, the door will open.

I'll position myself here, beside these nice drapes. It's hard to tell in this plush carpeting, but I hear the pitter-patter of shiny black shoes, and, yes, the door opens.

"Mr. Carson? Mr. Carson, are you here?"

It's rude to ring and run, but I don't want to try to explain. So, I'll slip into the corridor and head downstairs. Easy enough when you're black and incredibly agile.

Okay, the restaurant is to the right and…the watcher is sitting in the middle of the lobby holding a newspaper. He's positioned himself so he can see the elevators and the front door.

Let me get a good look at this guy. He's midthirties or so, handsome in an extreme way. And intense. He's a man who's used to having what he wants. Powerful. Those aren't shoulder pads in his suit. Neat appear-

ance. Fastidious might be more accurate. All in all, a sort of control freak. And one with enough patience to wait and watch. My guess is that this guy's after Celeste. Someone from her old life. Like maybe the fiancé she's trying to avoid.

The way I have it figured, he can't get to her room because she's booked under the Carson suite. So she's safe enough for the moment. But this buffoon needs to say sayonara, goodbye, or that's all folks, whichever language he prefers.

I have a plan. It's going to require minor damages and the split second timing I'm famous for, but then it keeps me in top form. As for the damages, well, it's for a worthy cause.

So, I slink across the lobby hoping not to draw attention to myself. And I jump up on the table behind the sofa where he's sitting. And I saunter along the table and brush against the vase of beautiful and exotic flowers, and, oh! no! I tip the vase on top of his head.

My goodness, but that man can holler. I suppose the water might have been a tad cool.

No time to talk. One great leap across the room, a skitter under a velvet love seat and a dash across the corridor and I'm home free, leaving one very wet watcher. I certainly hope he isn't allergic to lilies and roses.

One peek at my handiwork, and yes, I do believe he's going to have to go home, at least for a change of clothes.

Now back to GG. She was wearing an interesting necklace. It was some type of ring on a chain, and the more I think about it, the more I want to examine the image on the ring. There's more going on here than meets the eye—human or feline. And since I've jumped into the middle of this, I'm not leaving until I figure out the truth.

But one quick stop in the office for a phone call. Too bad I couldn't get that calling card I wanted. I suppose Ashley will have to accept a collect call. Ah, it's a small price to pay to know that I'm alive and well and tending to business.

Chapter Seven

Celeste awoke from the dream with a sense of foreboding. There had been blood and bullets in the dream, and she had been running. Dan had also been in the dream, and his mother. There were others she didn't know, but everyone was fighting or running.

As she shook back her long hair, she knew the dream meant trouble.

There were those in her family who had a gift for dreams that gave a glimpse into the future. Although Celeste respected that gift, all her life she'd tried to avoid it. She had not honed her talent or skill, but had preferred to let it lay dormant. But this dream could not be ignored. There was trouble in the future, for her and for Dan. This one time she wished she'd learned how to interpret and analyze, because she couldn't tell if the trouble came from Dan or herself.

Her hand went to the ring that dangled from a chain on her chest. Her mother would understand the dream. Maria was very gifted in such matters. But Celeste knew she would never burden her mother with the images of death and violence. Never. Such a dream would worry her mother sick.

She pushed back the sheets and stood, stretching.

For the first time she realized that Familiar was not in the room. She called him and looked under the bed and in the bathroom, then noticed the door to the stone balcony was ajar. For one heartstopping moment she feared he might have fallen to his death.

There was a faint scratching at the hallway door and the sound of a muffled meow, and she rushed to open the door. Familiar stood in the hall, tail twitching slightly.

"You'd better get in here," she said, scooping him into her arms. She buried her face in his dark fur and allowed herself the luxury of his rumbling purr. There was the rasp of his tongue on her forehead, and she drew back. The cat was regarding her with a golden gaze that seemed to show an intense intelligence.

"If I told you I dreamed of blood and death, what would you recommend?" she asked the cat.

"Meow." Familiar jumped down and went to the telephone. With one paw he flipped the receiver off.

"Call the police?" she asked.

The cat remained silent.

"Call home?"

Once again, Familiar didn't respond. Only his tail drummed on the bedside table.

"Impatient, aren't we?" she asked, laughing. "Should I call Mr. Carson?"

"Meow!" Familiar patted the phone pad as if to punch the buttons.

Celeste felt a rush of hope at the very idea. But she knew it was not rational to want to call a man she didn't know and go on about a dream. Even one in which he faced a gun.

That thought propelled her toward the phone. That one image of the dream was so vivid she could smell the tang of barbecue sauce. She was in a place she'd never been, but there was a vista of incredible beauty, and the sun was setting with the pinks and reds of a winter day. Indeed, she could feel the cold as she stood outside. Behind her there was the sizzle of meat cooking on a grill. And Dan was there, facing a stranger who pointed a gun at his heart. She knew the stranger would shoot, intended to shoot, and with pleasure. Dan was an impediment. He would be killed. And there was nothing she could do.

Celeste's hand trembled as she reached for the phone and fumbled in her purse for the card that Dan had given her. Carson Dynamics. It was a simple card with the address, his name and a phone number. She started to dial and then hung up the phone. "I can't." She shook her head, stroking Familiar's sleek coat. "It's only a dream, and I can't be certain it's true. If I call him and tell him this, he'll think I'm nuts or that I'm trying to win his sympathy. I can't do it." She stood up and began to pace the room.

"Maybe we should go get some lunch," Celeste finally said. "I'll take a shower and get dressed."

Familiar batted the leather-bound menu for room service.

Even though she was still worried about the dream, Celeste couldn't help laughing. "Room service. Yes, I see. You can't eat in the dining room, but you're hungry. That can of tuna I gave you wasn't exactly what you wanted. Okay, pick out what you want while I shower. That'll clear my head and then we'll dine in luxury."

In fifteen minutes she was tingling clean and felt more like herself. The past month had been like a page out of some Victorian novel where all of the forces of the universe had turned against her. But she had to think beyond the current mess. She had to find a future and aim toward that.

And she had to be honest with herself. She had been raised as the heir to the Levert name and all of the honor and authority that came with that. Walking away had been hard. She had learned the history of the Roma from the cradle, and she had accepted as hers the responsibility of leadership. It was, of course, a position that she would one day share with her husband. For all of the fact that Gypsies had traveled the world and lived on every continent, they were still a provincial people when it came to the roles of men and women. They were not ready to accept a female as their leader.

And she was not able to accept Trell Sylvest as a man who would lead her people, or her.

She sat down at the beautifully carved vanity and began to apply a light foundation and some eye makeup. Normally she didn't wear eye shadow during the day, but she thought the routine would sooth her, and the final result would make her feel prettier, happier. As she worked, her thoughts returned to her family.

That was the real problem. If her father had chosen a man with integrity or honor, Celeste knew she would have married and made the best of it—because that was her destiny. But Trell Sylvest was a man of questionable principles. She had known him in grade school as a bully. He'd taken pleasure in tormenting smaller and younger boys. In high school he'd dated the prettier girls, but his eye had always been on power more than romance. Even as a teenager he'd watched her more closely than she liked.

Those tendencies had made her dislike and distrust him then. And when they were older, he'd begun to follow her, showing up outside the houses of her friends, or at the beach when she went with a group of girls. He made it his business to know where she was going and what she was doing. The result was that she'd felt like a prisoner with a warden.

She'd taken all of this to her father. Ramone had only laughed at the schoolboy behavior, noting that children grew out of their mischief. He said that Trell followed her to offer protection, to make sure that she was safe. He admired Trell for such dedication.

Celeste knew better. Trell was guarding her as if she were already his prize. And she knew what marriage to him would be like. Even more important, she didn't believe he had the character to lead her people. And once she was married, she would lose all power to speak out. A Gypsy woman did not publicly defy her husband. It simply wasn't done.

So she had run away. In the back of her mind was the hope that Trell would give up. That he would marry another. But it was a vague hope, and when Celeste left her family, she had accepted that she might never return.

"Maybe Trell will move on to someone else," she said aloud. "Maybe he'll fall in a hole and disappear," she said, taking off the large robe she'd found in the bathroom and slipping into a long-sleeved red knit dress.

She picked up the bathrobe and noticed for the first time the small monogram on one cuff. D.C. Her fingers tightened in the fabric. It was Dan's. She knew instantly that he'd given her his suite, and she smiled at the gallant way he'd done it. Without even telling her. She'd simply signed the register where Diana had showed her. Unbidden, it occurred to her that he was the kind of man who would make a good leader—someone who sacrificed without asking for any credit. It was certainly a trait Trell Sylvest had not displayed.

"Tell me, Familiar," she said, "am I worrying about my family because I'm afraid to let my thoughts dwell on Dan Carson?"

"Meow."

"I know it's a normal reaction to be drawn to a man who appears to offer everything you need. I'm frightened and he seems so unafraid. I'm running and he offers stability. It's normal that I would feel attracted to him." Familiar came over and began to rub against her. "He demonstrates qualities that I admire. Like strength and kindness and generosity. Not to mention killer good looks. He's also a man who's successful and involved with his work. He's charming…exciting." She hesitated. That was the exact problem. Dan Carson seemed to have everything she could want. And even the thought of him gave her that little extra thrill. There was definitely a chemical thing going on between them, at least from her end. From his, too, if she were any judge.

"It has to be chemistry," she said aloud, earning another rub from Familiar. "I don't really know him. People can put up a false front. He may be a tyrant underneath all of his nice manners and kindness." But she knew he wasn't. The scary thing about Dan Carson was that he wasn't a stranger. She'd known him less than twenty-four hours, but she would have staked her future on his character. In fact, she had. "He scares me," she admitted. "No, that isn't right.

He doesn't scare me. My reaction to him is so strong that I unnerve myself.''

Familiar patted the menu with a paw. ''Meow!''

His cry was strident, and Celeste leaned over to examine the menu. She laughed aloud when she saw what his paw was on. ''Lobster?''

''Meow.''

''A cat with discriminating taste.''

''Meow!''

''Okay, I'll order it. You're lucky you were adopted by someone with a little money in the bank. A working girl couldn't afford to indulge your tastes.'' She placed the order for the lobster and a crab salad for herself. ''After lunch we should rent a car and take a drive around the city. I need to find a place to live.'' Celeste realized she was talking to the cat as if he understood, but he actually seemed to. At any rate, it made her feel better. ''I'm sure the concierge can arrange something for us to drive, and I'd feel better if I weren't mooching off Dan.'' She made a mental note to start referring to him as Mr. Carson. If she didn't put up a barrier to her own emotions, she feared she would set herself up for a big hurt.

The phone beside the bed rang sharply and Celeste immediately picked it up.

''You've walked into more trouble than you can imagine. My suggestion to you is to get out of Dan Carson's life and do it fast, while you still can.''

Celeste didn't have time to respond. The phone went dead in her hand.

DAN ENTERED the lobby of The Admiralty and headed for his room on the fourteenth floor. He needed pri-

vacy and a telephone, but mostly he needed to make
sure Celeste was okay.

Though he realized that she was running from her
own demons, Dan was now certain that Celeste had
more to fear from association with him than with anything from her past. If Kip was under surveillance, it
made sense that Celeste might also be—simply because she'd accepted his offer of help.

Anger at Rick Hanson flared again. The CIA agent
had dragged him into this, and now innocent people
were paying the price. Dan realized that his only option, once he was certain Celeste was safe, was to
come clean about Carson Dynamic's involvement in
the bad oil deal. The company's mistake was innocent. He was no longer willing to play Rick Hanson's
spy game.

As he got off the elevator and headed toward Celeste's suite, Dan felt anticipation tingle along his
body. He wanted to see her. It was ridiculous and
foolish, but he simply wanted to look at her. Well,
that wasn't true. He wanted to touch her, too. To kiss
her and hold her. It was a dangerous sign. She was
the most beautiful woman he'd ever seen. And so
damned determined to be independent.

He knocked lightly on the door and was surprised
when it swung open. Celeste stood before him, white-
faced and frightened.

"What?" he said, reaching out to grasp her shoulders before he thought. He could see that something
was terribly wrong. "What's happened?"

Celeste looked up at him, her eyes wide with fright.
"Someone just called me. They told me to get out of
your life."

Dan stepped into the room and shut the door. Even

though he'd suspected that Celeste had been drawn into the web of his life, he was still shocked. "A man or woman?" he asked.

"A man. And he sounded like he meant what he said."

"Can you remember exactly what he said?" Dan led her to the bed and eased her down so that she sat beside the black cat.

"He said that I had walked into trouble and that I should get away from you while I still could."

Dan felt the slight tremor that went through her and he knelt in front of her, his hands soothing her shoulders and then her silky hair. "It's okay," he said, feeling her body tremble. Even as he looked at her he saw her teeth begin to chatter and he eased up onto the bed so that he sat beside her. He put his arm around her and pulled her against his chest, his hand moving up and down her back. "It's okay," he said again.

At first she resisted, but then he slowly felt her yield to the comfort of his body. He could feel her heart beating rapidly against his chest, and he bent his head to whisper into her hair. "I don't know who would do such a thing, but I promise that no one will harm you." In that second, her safety was the most important thing he could imagine.

"What's going on?" she asked.

Dan hesitated. "It's a long story and it involves a business deal. I thought it was a bad idea to begin with, and now I'm certain it's one of the worst I've ever heard. By this afternoon, it'll all be taken care of."

"Why would they call me?" she asked. "I don't know anything about your business."

"Chances are they saw you get out of one of the company cars. It's just terrorist tactics." He lifted her face so that she gazed up into his eyes. Whatever he'd intended to say fled from his mind.

The only word he could think of was exotic. He'd never seen eyes such a golden shade of brown, and the dark lashes were long and thick. Looking down into her gaze, he felt as if he'd stepped from a high cliff and was falling, spiraling through the air. He didn't feel fear or worry; he was only aware of her beauty.

He felt a sharp pain on his chest and remembered the wound from the statue. It flared up at the oddest times.

He brought his lips down on hers as he closed his eyes. It was not something he'd meant to do, but he wasn't surprised. It was the most natural thing. And he felt her mouth open and accept him. Her arms moved up around his neck and her fingers burrowed into his hair, finally catching hold in a grip that sent a wave of pleasure through him.

He had never been so keenly aware of a woman. He could feel the slight lift of her rib cage as she breathed, the press of her soft breasts against him. One hand moved into her hair and the thick, heavy texture was like silk under water. His other hand moved to her back and he pressed her more firmly against him, feeling another jolt of pleasure as she responded so willingly.

Still holding her, he eased her slowly back onto the bed, his lips never leaving her. One hand supported her while the other began a slow exploration of her waist, gradually moving higher.

As his fingers brushed her breast, he felt her tremble again, and the blood pounded harder in his veins. There was a tiny portion of him that knew he should stop. But he was too far gone. This wasn't something he'd planned, or even consciously sought. But he could no longer deny his own need for her. Whatever strange power Celeste Sanchez exerted on him, he was completely under her spell.

CELESTE LACED her fingers in his thick hair and clung to him. What was happening was insane. This was a stranger, a man who would be her boss. But common sense was no counterweight to the demands of her body.

As he eased her back onto the bed, she gave up all thoughts of ending the kiss. She gave herself completely to the pleasure of his touch. His lips demanded her attention at the same time his hand began to move slowly up her body. His touch teased and promised as his mouth moved down to her neck and then lower as his hand began to work the small buttons of the dress, freeing her to his warm kisses.

He moved her dress aside and paused as he lifted the chain that held her ring. Before he had a chance to examine it, Celeste slipped the necklace off and tossed it out of the way.

As his mouth found her breast, Celeste had the sensation that she was dreaming. Her body was electric. Dan's slightest touch generated a need that was greater than anything she'd ever experienced. Her hands reached to the buttons of his shirt and she began to undress him. In a moment his bare chest was against her, and the gentle friction of their skin only made her want him more.

Her hands moved to his waist and she began to

unbuckle his belt as he drew back from her. In a moment her dress was unbuttoned and lying on the floor.

She stared into his eyes. She'd never seen anything so blue, so alive, so on fire with the promise of pleasure. It came to her that she was acting on impulse, on a physical desire, and she didn't care. Her feelings for Dan were irrational, perhaps borne of desperation and the need to cling to someone. That didn't matter, either. She found that she was panting lightly as they stared at each other. Then her hands went to his zipper and she began to finish undressing him. Her palms glided over the sensitive skin of his lean hips and taut abdomen, dipping lower until she made him moan with pleasure and need.

The knock at the door was brisk yet soft.

Celeste felt Dan tense, and she had a sudden premonition that her dream had somehow come true. Then she remembered. "Room service," she whispered, silently cursing the timing of the food delivery.

"Leave it in the hall," Dan called out.

There was another knock.

"Leave it," Dan said, this time with more impatience in his voice.

"Dan, is that you?"

Celeste felt the tension in Dan and then she recognized the voice as belonging to Diana Carson.

Chapter Eight

Dan shifted his weight off the bed and slowly stood. His desire for Celeste was like a drug. Even as he glanced toward her, lying against the dark sheets of the bed, he felt an almost uncontrollable need to return to her. One more kiss, one more touch, the feel of her hair against his skin. She was the most beautiful woman he'd ever seen. But even as his blood pounded, a cool note of reason had returned. There was no doubt that his feelings for Celeste Sanchez were deep and sincere. He didn't question them. Even though he'd known her for such a short time, he was falling in love with her. He'd never experienced such desire, but it was so much more. He accepted that he was beginning to love her in a way that happened only once in a lifetime—and, tragically, this was all the more reason for him to get as far away from her as possible.

The memory of Shawna chilled his heart and almost paralyzed him with dread.

"It's your mother," Celeste whispered. She got out of bed and picked up her dress and underwear. "Dan, are you okay?"

He gathered his clothing and began to put it on.

"Take the bathroom," he said. "I'll take care of this." He forced his limbs to move, his voice to sound normal. When Celeste had closed the bathroom door and his clothes were back in place, he opened the door. He had regained his composure. Diana Carson stood by the room service tray. Although she smiled, Dan could see the worry in her face.

"I thought I'd take Celeste to lunch and then show her some of the places for rent in Houston. I didn't realize you'd be here."

Dan stepped aside as his mother pushed the cart into the room. Diana had never been a mother who suffocated or controlled. Once he'd reached adulthood, she'd backed off and treated him with the respect one adult shows another. She had never, not a single time, interfered in his private life, or even questioned him about it. But he had to wonder at her appearance at the hotel. She also wasn't in the habit of playing adoptive mother to new employees.

"Where's Celeste?" Diana asked, looking around the room.

"In the bathroom." Dan realized the rumpled bed told its own story, but he was too old to hide or explain. "This isn't a good time," he said as gently as he could.

"I'm sorry, Dan. I had no idea you were here." She edged toward the door. "Tell Celeste that I'll call and see if I can help her find a place. I honestly was trying to be helpful."

The bathroom door opened and Celeste walked into the room. Dan could detect a flush on her olive skin, but she smiled at his mother. "You're very considerate, Mrs. Carson."

"Perhaps it would be best if you went with Mother

to look at some places. The sooner you get settled, the better it will be for everyone.''

At the tone of Dan's voice, so cool and formal, Celeste stared at him. Diana, too, gave him a curious look.

"That sounds like a good plan," Celeste said carefully.

"You're going to do fine at Carson Dynamics," Diana said, obviously trying to ease the tense situation. "I hadn't realized you'd ordered lunch already." She looked questioningly at the room service cart.

"Familiar was hungry," Celeste said. She looked around the room. "Where is that cat?"

For the first time, Dan realized that he hadn't seen Familiar since he entered the room. He'd opened the door and the only thing he'd seen had been Celeste. Nothing else had existed. It was as if he'd stepped into a vortex of whirling emotion, and even now, as he looked at Celeste, he felt a pulse of passion. For Celeste's safety, he was going to have to get control of the situation.

"Kitty, kitty." Celeste walked out onto the balcony, but there was no sign of the feline. "He must have gone out the door when one of you came in," she said as she came back in the room.

Dan heard the hint of panic in her voice. "We'll find him. I'll tell the hotel staff, and they'll do a thorough job of hunting for him. He's not your average cat, Celeste, I'm sure he'll be fine." Dan saw the worry on her face and all his resolve to harden his heart toward her failed. He walked over and put his hand on her shoulder. It was meant to be a reassuring gesture, but the merest touch of her was high voltage.

He saw the awareness in her eyes, which only fueled his own.

"I shouldn't leave until I find him," she said.

"I'll stay and look," Dan assured her. "Go on and explore Houston. You'll feel better about everything when you have your own place." Dan felt as if he were being torn in half. One part wanted to keep her at The Admiralty, to close the door of the room and finish what they'd started. The saner, safer part of him knew that if she wasn't out of his reach, he'd never be able to resist her. And he'd learned the hard way what happened to women he loved.

Diana walked briskly to the door, and Celeste started to follow. After two steps, she turned back.

Dan saw the confusion in her face. He understood why. They'd almost made love, and now he was treating her like a stranger. Worse than a stranger.

"Dan?" she touched his arm.

"Just go," he said softly, stepping away from her touch. The tiny wound he'd received in the maze on the Redwing Estate gave a hard tweak of pain. "For both of our sakes," he added more softly.

He wasn't certain, but he thought he saw the sheen of tears in her eyes as she quickly turned away and stepped into the hallway after his mother.

SO I COULDN'T take the heat the two lovebirds were generating and did the balcony escape route again. And I pulled the room service cord, again. So now they're putting in a work order to make sure there's not a short in the room service system. Ah, the wonders of modern technology. And none of them managed to see a sleek black cat flitting about the hotel. Is it that the bipeds simply don't look? I think it's a type of superiority complex—they're the only truly interesting species, at least to themselves, so they fail to notice a cat in a hallway. Fascinating.

Dogs, with their slobbering and completely inferior brain, can at least smell a cat or an intruder. Not the homo sapiens. Oh, well, I could go on about this all day.

My real concern is the flame building between Celeste and Dynamic Dan. Those two act like they've been doused in gasoline and set on fire. And I'm afraid that with two such highly combustible elements, the blaze will burn out of control. And we all know what happens when fire gets out of hand— someone gets burned. I, personally, do not think this is a good thing.

I've been around a lot of couples falling in love, but I've never seen anything to match the heat between these two. You'd almost think that someone had cast a spell on them. Of course, there's no such thing as a spell. I learned that during my travels to the Salem witch trials.

While those two are spending the lunch hour playing with matches—egads! Lunch! My lobster should be headed up to the room shortly. I've already missed breakfast due to the near plane crash. And I didn't believe it when I heard that airlines were getting chintzy on the onboard meals.

Now lunch calls for action. I'm going down to the kitchen right this minute to find something to dine on. I also want to make sure no one is watching Celeste. I'm such a busy boy. But I have my priorities straight—food first.

"NOW THIS IS a bungalow. More of a Hollywood-style house from the 1930s, but perfect for a single person,'' Diana said as the car stopped in front of a cute house set back from the street.

''It's lovely,'' Celeste agreed. The house was perfect. Exactly what she needed, but she couldn't manage to work up much enthusiasm. Her thoughts were on Dan. She'd never experienced someone who ran so hot—and then so cold. She felt as if she'd been physically bruised, but she knew it was only her emotions.

''This one is perfect, Diana,'' Celeste said, surprising even herself. ''And you said it was possible for a six-month lease?''

''Yes, the owner would love to sell, and if you decide to buy, then the six-month lease could be applied to the purchase price.''

Celeste raised her eyebrows. ''That's very generous of the owner. Are you sure?''

''Absolutely. You see, I happen to be the owner.'' Diana laughed. ''Don't look so startled. I'm an investor, and real estate is the market that makes or breaks an investor.''

''It certainly can be risky.'' Celeste wasn't surprised to find that Diana invested in property. She was surprised that the woman would sell investment property.

''I'm cautious.''

''Why are you willing to sell this particular house?'' Celeste asked.

''To be completely honest, I think this neighborhood has plateaued. Values will increase here but it will be a slow rise. The area has achieved stability. When I bought it, it was undervalued. I'll make money, and one of my employees will get a good place to live.''

''Are you always this generous to Carson Dynamic employees?''

Diana assessed her and the question. ''Our policy is to value each employee. We try to offer opportunity for growth and experimentation. And we know that happy employees are the most productive. Yes, we've helped others with living arrangements. It's part of our total theory of employment.''

Celeste hadn't expected such a serious answer, but she couldn't help but be impressed. ''It's a wonderful policy.''

''I think you'll be happy with us. Of course, if you're not, we'll help you relocate.''

Celeste knew it wasn't her imagination, there was something in Diana's tone. Something that begged her to probe further.

''Is there a reason I might not be happy at Carson Dynamics?''

Diana leaned back against the leather car seat. ''I'm glad you asked. I want you to understand that I don't interfere in my son's private affairs. Or at least I never have before. This time, though, I see that Dan is…has been overwhelmed. I can clearly see that his feelings for you are very strong.''

Celeste swallowed but said nothing. She watched Diana's dark eyes. Their gazes locked, then Diana's shifted away.

''Has Dan said anything to you about why he's a single man?''

This was not what Celeste had expected. She'd thought Diana was headed toward the inadvisability of an employee having an affair with the boss of the company. "No," she answered simply.

Diana looked out the window as if she were gathering her thoughts. "Ten years ago Dan was to be married. He'd fallen deeply in love with a young woman who shared his interest in business. Shawna Wright. She was a lovely girl, as bright as could be."

Diana stopped, and when Celeste could bear it no longer, she asked, "What happened?" She felt as if the older woman were playing her, but she couldn't help herself. There was something in Dan's past, she'd sensed it all along.

"Shawna was killed in an automobile accident on the way to the church. I can tell you, it was one of the worst days in my life. I can't imagine what it was like for Dan."

Celeste could. She could too easily visualize Dan at the church, waiting for his bride who would never come. So this, then, was the sadness in Dan, the reticence. "What an awful thing."

"To make it worse, Dan believes he's responsible."

"You said it was an automobile accident." Celeste was stunned. "He couldn't possibly think he made that happen."

Diana shook her head lightly. "Oh, but he can, and he does. And the terrible thing is that he might be right."

Celeste felt her temper flare, and she spoke without weighing her words. "How can you say that? You're his mother. How can you sit there and even imply that he could be responsible for an auto accident?"

"There's something about my family you should know," Diana said slowly. "I won't have Dan assume another load of guilt if something happens to you. Dan didn't believe in the curse when he fell in love with Shawna. When she accepted his proposal and agreed to marry him, Dan told me that I was silly to let the words of a jealous rival ruin my life.''

"What are you talking about?" Celeste couldn't believe what she was hearing. This sounded like something the older members of her family might say. Not a sophisticated businesswoman.

"A long time ago, when my husband was a young man, he met a woman. For my husband, it was a summer romance, something that bloomed and faded. For her, it was deeper. When I met Jake, he was over this other young woman. We fell in love. But she couldn't forget him. And she couldn't forgive him for not loving her. It seems she'd given up a lot for him, had sacrificed more than he knew. At any rate, she cursed him, and me, and our children. She said that we would suffer tragedy in love.'' Diana finally looked at Celeste, and there were tears in her eyes. "So far, it's been true.''

"I can't believe this,'' Celeste said. Her hand went to the handle of the car door. "Surely you know that curses don't exist.''

Diana didn't flinch. "That's exactly what Dan said. Until Shawna was killed.''

Celeste kept her voice low and even. "I'm sure the death of a young woman is a tragic thing. But you said it was ten years ago. Do you think your son should go on living his life as if he could never love another woman? Is this what you want for him?" Celeste had a horrible feeling that perhaps Diana Carson was more involved in her son's life than he understood.

"You're thinking that I don't want Dan to marry." Diana nodded slowly. "I can understand why you'd think that. But it isn't true. I'm only telling you this because I can see that Dan already has feelings for you. He's not a rash or emotional man. He's not impulsive. He cares for you. But if something happened to you, he'd never forgive himself."

"And what do you think might happen to me?" Celeste asked, feeling the first true uneasiness. Was it possible that Diana Carson was threatening her?

Diana reached across the seat and firmly touched her hand. "I sincerely hope nothing. I admit that the plane incident has rattled me. Someone put a drug in the pilot's coffee. That's not an accident. And this occurs just at the time Dan meets you and offers you a job. Please understand that Dan isn't in the habit of recruiting employees. Think about it, Celeste. I'm not trying to frighten you. But there's something at work here. As Dan's mother, I do have his vested interests at heart."

"Do you think I'm responsible for what happened on the plane?" Celeste felt the weight of her own guilt. It could have been her. Dan had convinced her otherwise, but all her doubts and fears returned. She felt as if she were suffocating in the close confines of the car.

"No. I'm not saying that at all. What I'm trying to do is be honest with you. Dan would have told you all of this eventually, though he would have spared you as long as he could. I was afraid, that during that time, if something did happen, Dan would forever blame himself. Now, at least I can tell him that you stayed with your eyes wide open."

"Yes, you've informed me about the curse." Celeste couldn't help the twinge of sarcasm.

"My daughter was left at the altar, an incident she never recovered from. Dan's older brother was also emotionally scarred, when his bride-to-be took a job in Hollywood and left him. Not two months later she married his best friend. My own husband died in a sailing accident when he was only forty-nine years old. These may all be coincidences, but it has made believers out of me and my children. Scoff if you want to. I wouldn't blame you if you did. But please don't endanger my son. Not his health or his heart."

Celeste eased back against the seat. The passion in Diana Carson's voice sounded real. Her love for Dan was beyond dispute. And her facts, if they were true, seemed beyond the bounds of mere coincidence. Celeste realized that she didn't believe in the idea of a curse, but she was beginning to understand how a string of such tragedies could make those affected believe.

Diana pressed the intercom button to the driver. "We're ready to go now," she said. She turned to Celeste. "I'll have the paperwork on the house drawn up. I'm assuming you'll be at work tomorrow?"

Celeste nodded. She wasn't at all sure she should stay in Houston, much less work at Carson Dynamics. The smartest thing to do might be to cut her losses and keep moving. There were plenty of other towns, plenty of other jobs.

But there was only one Dan Carson, and she knew by the pounding of her heart and the turmoil of her blood that it was too late to save herself from falling in love with him.

DAN SAT ON the side of the bed and tried to think of the best action to take. He'd come to the hotel to check on Celeste and call Rick Hanson and tell him the deal was off.

Somehow, in his attempt to comfort Celeste because of the threatening phone call, he'd found himself in bed with her, making love the only thing on his mind. He rubbed his forehead and tried to figure out how he'd moved from one course of action to another so fast.

The tiny mark, hardly visible, where he'd been stabbed by the statue in the maze, pulsed. It was ridiculous that such a tiny wound should flare up at the most ridiculous times. Whenever he was around Celeste.

He stood and began to pace the room. Hotel security was hot on the trail of Familiar. The cat had been in the kitchen, swiped a lobster and disappeared. With some careful questioning, Dan had ascertained that another strange incident in the hotel had occurred involving a huge vase of flowers that had mysteriously slid across a table and tipped on top of a man, an unregistered guest.

Dan couldn't prove it, but he suspected that Familiar had something to do with that episode.

At the sound of faint scratching on the door, Dan opened it and saw the black cat sitting in the hallway, waiting for admittance.

"You've got the place in a stir," he said.

"Meow." Familiar walked past him and hopped onto the bed. Digging beneath the spread, the cat began batting at something in the sheets.

"A discovery?" Dan asked as he pulled back the spread and found the object of the cat's attention. He picked up the gold chain that Celeste had been wearing. Dangling on it was a large gold ring. He remembered the feel of the ring against his chest. He'd assumed it was some type of locket. And he remembered how odd Celeste had acted about it when he'd touched it. As if it were secret.

He shifted so that he could get a good look at it under the light. The face of the ring was centered with an ornate cross, and letters were carved around the cross. Dan finally made them out. "Levert," he said, wondering if it was a code word or something in another language.

"Meow!" Familiar stepped up on his leg and batted at the ring.

"It looks like some kind of family crest," Dan said, wondering what significance the ring had for Celeste. She'd certainly been secretive about it. He let the gold chain pool into his palm as he lowered the ring. His fingers curled around it. "Levert," he repeated.

It was worth a try. It might be a long shot, but he had nothing to lose, and he knew Sanchez wasn't her last name. Though he knew the smart thing would be to banish Celeste from his thoughts and heart, he also knew it would be impossible.

Before he made any inquiries into Celeste's past, he had some unfinished business with Rick Hanson. He started to go to his room, but the desk in the corner had a company computer with all of his files. It would be much more convenient to work from here, and Celeste wouldn't be back for several hours, he was sure.

He walked to the desk and flipped on the computer.

As he began going through documents, he found Rick Hanson's number and punched it into the telephone.

In a moment he was speaking with the CIA agent. "Hanson, this is Dan Carson. I'm calling to tell you the deal is off."

"Just like that?" Hanson sounded amused.

"Yes, just like that." Dan snapped his fingers for effect. "Find another goat to use as bait. I quit."

"You're willing to allow your mother to be prosecuted for her involvement in purchasing illegal oil?"

Dan hated the smarmy tone the CIA agent took. "My mother made a mistake. But it was made in innocence, and I believe that any jury in the nation will believe her. I've decided we'll take our chances and go to trial."

There was silence, and Dan began to feel uneasy. Rick Hanson was giving up too easily. The CIA agent had struck him as a man who would resort to worse and worse threats.

"What if I told you that we have evidence your mother knew the oil was illegal?" Hanson said.

"I'd say you're a liar," Dan snapped.

"It's true. We have taped phone conversations."

For a moment Dan expected the agent to admit it was a joke, or that he was lying. When there was only another long silence, Dan said, "Then you made it up. My mother may be naive, but she isn't a crook. We don't need the money bad enough to break the law."

"Maybe you'd like to hear the tapes before you make your decision."

Dan gripped the phone. "Maybe I would. Maybe that's what I insist on."

"That would be nice, Mr. Carson, but I'm afraid

there isn't time. As I understand it, the deal is set for Sunday. We've learned from our sources that Norris will push the meeting time forward to Saturday afternoon. Tomorrow.''

"I can be on a plane to Washington within the hour," Dan said. "You seem to think I'm stupid. I'm not meeting anyone at any time until I see and hear those tapes you claim you have. I'm beginning to see that you're pulling another bluff.''

"It's not a bluff.''

"I don't believe you. It's been a pleasure, but our business is concluded." Dan started to put the receiver down.

"Carson, it's too late to back out. Your name is already being bantered around by people who would have no qualms about walking into a restaurant and killing a hundred people just to take you out. They would kill your mother, your employees, they'd bomb your building or try to bring down a commercial plane if they thought you were on board. You seem to forget that if you back out now, these men will assume that you pulled the plug on them. They'll blame you and you alone. And you'll be out there all by yourself, without any assistance from us. Do you understand?''

Chapter Nine

Dan stared at the telephone. It wasn't that Rick Hanson had left him without options. Dan knew he could pull out of the scheme and weather any consequences Hanson or the CIA could throw at him. The accusations and lies would damage him and the company, but Dan knew he could endure it. It was his mother who would suffer.

The CIA agent had made it very clear that Dan's choice could endanger innocent people. For how long? How many months would have to pass before he could walk on the street or attend a movie or a play without the thought at the back of his mind that bystanders could be killed because of him?

With the full weight of the price of his decision, Dan also found the resolve to turn the situation to his advantage. In business, he'd learned that the art of making a deal was to never yield control to the other party. This situation was no different—as long as he could look at it as business.

He got up and went to the bed. A lingering trace of Celeste's perfume caught him unprepared and the rush of emotion left him breathless. He picked up the gold chain and the ring again. Levert. What did it mean? He put the jewelry on the bedside table and remembered the way Celeste had looked against the sheets with the faint gleam of the necklace between her breasts. Something was happening between them that needed attention. Serious attention.

But Celeste would have to wait a day or two, until he'd resolved his immediate problem. And then, whatever it took, he would deal with the Carson Curse and his own fears. With that in mind, he walked to the phone and dialed Kip's number. When the pilot answered, he dove right in. "The man who's watching you, is he still there?"

"He's out there. I don't know who taught him to do surveillance, but he needs a better teacher."

Dan smiled. Kip didn't have a lot of tolerance for people who were less than professional. "We're going to use him to our advantage. Are you feeling up to leading a wild-goose chase?"

"That's exactly the medicine I need."

"Good, go to the airport and get the plane ready for takeoff. File a flight plan for Cincinnati."

"Ohio?" Dan asked.

"That's the place."

"Why are we going there?"

"We're not. But we want the people who're keeping tabs on us to think that's our destination."

"Exactly," Kip said, laughing at the idea of it. "I like this. So, where are we really going?"

Dan didn't want to divulge this part of his plan. Not yet. Kip would argue and kick and try to figure a way around it. "I'm not sure," he said.

"Okay, I'll take care of that. Then what?"

"This Kenneth Martin, the cop. Did you find out anything else about him?" Dan asked.

"Aside from the fact there's no such cop? It was obviously an alias. False badge, false ID. I haven't gotten any further than that."

Dan found that tidbit very interesting. "Keep plugging away. I'm going to put a couple of men on another project. Does the word *Levert* mean anything to you?"

There was silence as Kip thought it over. "Nope. Not a word I've ever heard. What does it mean?"

"I don't know, but I'll find out," Dan promised. Dan's hand hesitated on the phone as he considered his options. Rick Hanson had planted the seed of doubt in his mind that Celeste was not who she claimed to be. Dan knew she was using an assumed name. That didn't matter. But he had to be certain she was a woman escaping domestic strife, not someone who was involved in the oil mess. She certainly didn't seem the type, but then, if she was a spy, she wouldn't.

He lifted the receiver and dialed the office. "Betty, I need you to do some research for me," he said to his secretary. He could trust Betty to do the most delicate work, and to keep her mouth shut.

"Sure," she said, anticipation in her tone.

"It's a word. *Levert.* It might be a company or a person or it could be an acronym for something else."

"You don't have a clue where to begin?" Betty asked. "What does it relate to?"

"A ring, and a symbol of a cross."

"A man's ring?"

"That's right. A gold ring with this ornate cross and the letters in a half-moon around the cross."

"I'll see what I can find," she said.

"Thanks." Dan replaced the phone and felt a

twinge of conscience. Somehow, it seemed he'd betrayed Celeste. But with so much at stake, he didn't have a choice. He had to be certain who she was before he found himself so deeply in love with her that it ended up endangering everyone he loved.

I'M NOT SURE that Dynamic Dan has made the best decision here. It's one thing for him to ask my Goddess about the ring, but quite another to investigate her. I have the feeling she'd tell him all about herself, if he'd only ask.

Humans have the finesse of a hog stampeding on the way to the trough. They have much to learn from the feline species, but I doubt they ever will. A cat will sit for hours, watching, observing. Sometimes we appear to doze, our eyes mere slits as we purr or simply sit. But we are not sleeping. We are gathering data.

It's a task that requires great patience and keen powers of observation. These are two traits I've found even my beloved humans to be very short on. Dynamic Dan is a man who's used to snapping his fingers and having his desires attended to. The Goddess is used to avoiding direct confrontation at all costs. Her needs are never considered. Whatever her life has been in the past, she's been a pawn. I know these things. I wonder why Dan can't see them.

I suppose it makes sense that Dan wouldn't easily recognize Celeste's method of dealing with life because he's never, not a single time, considered what it might be like to be powerless. And the reverse is true of the Goddess. One thing for certain, though, she will feel completely violated and exposed if she discovers that Dan is investigating her. And I feel *responsible for this turn of events. I should have kept the ring to myself. But I was curious, too. And you know the old saying, curiosity killed the cat.*

At least Dan hasn't stooped to going through her personal things. Uh-oh. I think I spoke too soon. He's headed for her luggage. I'd better do something fast. I really hate to ruin his good pants. Dan is a snappy dresser, and as a cat in formal attire, I like a guy who knows how to choose a wardrobe. Speaking of wardrobe, I have to get him out of Celeste's. She could come in at any moment.

And I don't want to exercise after eating two lobsters. I'm getting too old for this, but here goes.

"HEY! HEY!" Dan felt the cat's sharp claws in his calf and whirled around. To his amazement, Familiar hung on, digging his sharp claws in deeper.

"Familiar!" Dan leaned down and captured the cat, carefully extracting the claws and lifting him in his arms. "What's wrong with you?"

Familiar lifted a paw and put it against Dan's cheek. He applied just the tiniest hint of pressure.

Dan walked to the bed and put the cat down on it. "What's going on with you?" He stroked the cat's fur and then walked back to the luggage he'd placed on the rack. He felt like a criminal, going through Celeste's things, but he had to.

Before he could even unzip the case, the cat was on his leg again. This time the claws were sharper and the teeth had come into play. "Hey!" Dan hopped across the room, fell onto the bed and then turned to extract the cat once again. He found it interesting that as soon as he abandoned the luggage, Familiar quit biting.

He picked the cat up and held him at arm's length. "I think you're trying to tell me something. And I think you think I'm too dumb for a subtle gesture."

Dan was amazed when the cat meowed and seemed to nod his head. He put him down on the bed. "I don't like snooping into her things, either. But it's a case of necessity. If she's not who she says she is, a lot of people could get hurt. I think the odds justify snooping this time."

"Me-ee-ow!" Familiar put a small growl on the end.

"You disagree." Dan saw that it was obvious the cat did. But the cat couldn't possibly understand. He turned back to the case and even before he'd gone two steps, he felt as if he'd been slugged between the shoulder blades by a hammer.

As he stumbled across the room, he realized the cat had launched himself at him. Stunned, he turned around to find Familiar at the door.

Dan didn't have a second to gather his thoughts as the door opened and Celeste walked in. At the sight of Dan she stopped. He was completely unprepared to see her. He'd expected his mother to keep her occupied for the rest of the afternoon. And she was evidently surprised to find him in the room she was using. They had parted on an awkward note. Dan remembered his coolness, his attempt to regain control. And he knew he'd wounded her. But he didn't know how to handle the situation, and he could see that she was as lost as he was.

In all of the confusion, there was only one thing that was clear to him—he wanted her. The sight of her, standing in the doorway, tentative and so vulnerable, made him feel as if every inch of skin had suddenly come alive. Her touch, the delicate scent of her perfume, the feel of her hair, it was as if he were assaulted by the sensations. Dan took a half step backward, revealing the piece of luggage he'd been about to open.

He saw her look at the suitcase and then at him. She knew exactly what he'd intended to do. There was no explanation, no way that he could make her understand. He saw that now, and he was painfully aware of the violation he'd committed. Trust was the foundation of any relationship, whether it was business, friendship or love. And he'd just sledgehammered any hope he'd ever had that Celeste would trust him by demonstrating that he didn't trust her.

"Dan?" she said softly, her voice breaking.

He'd never felt as guilty in his life. He had to think of something to say. He had to make an attempt.

Before he could speak, Familiar leaped across the room and landed on the suitcase. Yowling and hissing, the cat attacked the piece of luggage with the frenzy of a demon.

"Familiar!" Celeste rushed into the room and made a grab for the cat. "Familiar," she said, "What's wrong?" She looked at Dan. "What's he after the luggage for?"

"I don't know," he answered honestly. Grabbing fast he was able to nab the cat. In one fluid gesture he brought Familiar to his chest and held him closely. As soon as his hands were on the cat, Familiar settled down and began to purr. Dan looked down at the cat in astonishment. Familiar's big golden eyes stared up at him and then one winked.

"What's going on here?" Celeste asked as she stared at Dan and the cat.

"Maybe Familiar had a reaction to too much lobster. Maybe he thought the luggage was a crustacean." Dan knew he sounded foolish, but he kept talking. "Apparently Familiar found a lobster in the hotel kitchen and ran off with it. I got a full report from the staff about the incident." He had, and it had amused him. "He still seemed hungry, so I gave him the food you'd ordered from room service."

"Another lobster?"

"And some of the crab salad." Dan shook his head. "He wanted it." Food wasn't the cause of Familiar's behavior. The cat had just saved his bacon. He looked down into the golden eyes and thought he saw a hint of humor—and more than a hint of superiority.

"Dan, he's only a cat." Celeste stepped forward and lifted Familiar from his arms. "That's enough food for a half dozen people."

"Horses will eat until they get sick. Cats and dogs are supposed to regulate their intake." He thought about it a minute and realized that his mother's dog, Pookie, would eat anything it could swallow. Shoes, remote controls, flower arrangements, oriental carpets. Pookie's tastes were varied and voracious. "At least I thought they managed their own diets."

"We have no idea if Familiar is used to eating such rich foods." Celeste petted the cat. "And I haven't made any real effort to find his owners." She bent her head so that she was rubbing a cheek against Familiar's ears.

Dan started to reach out to her and stopped himself. If he actually touched her, he wouldn't be able to stop.

"I wonder what's in my luggage that Familiar is so wild about," she said.

Dan managed a shrug. "I don't know. He just went after the case like a maniac." The words were ashes on his tongue. It was wrong to lie to Celeste, but this time a falsehood was far better than the truth.

"So, you were going to investigate?" Celeste looked at him with brows arched.

"I was," he said.

Celeste laughed. "Maybe he has a shoe fetish."

Dan gave a weak grin. "Maybe so. Did you find any houses you liked?"

Celeste turned away from him and walked to the bed where she deposited the cat and then moved away from it. Dan was acutely aware of her actions and knew that she, too, was putting as much distance between herself and the bed as possible. "Your mother showed me some lovely places. I was amazed to find that Carson Dynamics helps employees with housing."

"One of the perks," Dan said. He could see that something else had happened between Celeste and Diana. "Is something wrong?"

"Maybe I shouldn't try to work for your company, Dan. You've been very kind to me. Very generous. But you don't know what kind of employee I am. You haven't even asked about my education. I'm mostly self-taught. I don't have college degrees."

"That doesn't matter." This was something Dan firmly believed. "School is wonderful, and sometimes a great shortcut to knowledge, but it isn't the only place a person can learn. Life is always the best teacher." He reached out to Celeste and then dropped his hand. "You'll be an asset to Carson Dynamics."

Celeste nodded but failed to meet his gaze. She looked suddenly overwhelmed. More than anything, Dan wanted to comfort her. But he knew he couldn't risk it.

"I have to get to the office. There are some things I need to take care of. I'll have Betty prepare all the paperwork for you to sign tomorrow. You know, insurance, retirement, all of those tedious but necessary things."

"Thanks," Celeste said in a voice that sounded tired.

"Get some rest. I'll give you a call later and make sure you're comfortable. If you need anything, Celeste, the company has an account here. Get it and you can pay us back when you're on your feet."

"You're more than generous," she said, finally looking at him. Her gaze was like a touch. He saw her eyes widen and a flush creep over her skin. He, too, felt as if he'd stepped closer to a furnace.

"I'll see you later." He hurried out of the hotel room and closed the door, leaning against the wall for a moment as he collected himself. It was a good thing he was going to be gone from the office. He wouldn't be able to work if Celeste was within a hundred yards of him.

THE CAT'S PURR soothed Celeste as she sat on the edge of the bed and held him. She had gotten herself into a fine mess. She couldn't even look at her boss without trembling. Her boss's mother, who was also her boss, had all but warned her that Dan's affections could be deadly—and what was that all about, anyway?

Celeste looked at the phone. More than anything

she wanted to call home. Diana's talk of curses had greatly unsettled her. Her people had a long history of casting curses and telling fortunes, but Celeste knew that most of the "powers" of predicting the future were simply the abilities of an astute person to ask the right questions. There were, of course, people who were more gifted than others, those with special sensitivity. Celeste accepted her own ability to select stocks and investments. She couldn't say how she did it, she just knew that one was a better choice than another.

There were those among the Roma who told stories of the elders who could cast a spell or curse, but Celeste had assumed that these were the romantic stories of her clan. They were generally stories of love or about finding unexpected wealth. But there were also the more unsettling tales of revenge.

She stood up and began to pace the room. Her people called such curses *amria.* She had not heard that word since she was a child. But her mother would know if such a thing were possible—to curse an entire line and bring such unhappiness down on a family.

She remembered the way Dan had looked as she walked into the room—as if he'd been caught with his hand in the cookie jar. Such strange behavior.

Not to mention the way he'd kissed her. His lips had melted her resistance. No man had ever had such an effect on her, and even in memory, it made her breathing shallow, her heart race.

Yet he'd turned as cold as stone toward her.

She pondered the change in him, wondering if his mother had evoked the cold response. It was almost impossible for her to judge, because she knew so little about the ways of the *gajikane.* That was her people's word for foreigners, and Celeste had never thought she would use it. But she'd never realized how inadequate she was to confront the issues of living outside the narrow confines of the world into which she'd been born.

Was there something wrong between Diana and Dan? How could she judge when her own experience had been that her father had chosen her husband-to-be—a man she despised. Was Diana merely trying to frighten her away because she didn't approve of the idea that Dan might care for her? It was very complicated, and Celeste felt at a loss to figure out how to deal with it.

When the knock came at the door, Celeste was relieved at the idea that something would force her out of the twist of her own thoughts.

"Who is it?" she asked.

"Rick Hanson, CIA."

Celeste felt her heart lurch. The CIA! What were they doing looking for her? Panic made her hurry to the door and open it wide. The man who stood there looked angry and intense.

"Where's Dan Carson?" he asked sharply.

"What do you want?" Celeste countered. She didn't like the man or his attitude.

"I'm a federal agent and I have business with Carson. Tell me where he is or face charges of obstructing an investigation."

Celeste had never had a run-in with the authorities. Centuries of persecution by law officers all over the world had left her people with a cautious distrust. "I don't know." She started to close the door.

Rick Hanson was faster. He put his hand out and

caught the solid wood with ease. "I don't suppose you're aware how much trouble Carson is in?"

"I don't know what you mean and I'm not in a position to discuss Mr. Carson's troubles or anything else about him."

"He's about to go to prison, and you just might be going with him."

Celeste didn't believe the words, but the cold light in the agent's eyes made her hesitate. "Prison? For what?"

"Mr. Carson and his company have been involved in smuggling oil into this country."

"I don't believe you." Celeste didn't. She knew instinctively that Dan was not a crook. His personal life she couldn't fathom, but she trusted his business judgment implicitly.

"You think he's too noble to be involved in such a thing?" the agent asked with an ugly edge in his voice.

"I do," Celeste answered. "Now leave. I don't have to hear this. I won't listen anymore." She made an effort to close the door, but once again the man blocked her.

"Were you aware that he asked me to check up on you?"

Celeste tried to hide her shock but she knew she wasn't successful. She could see the agent's satisfaction. He was a man who relished the ugliness of his job. She was suddenly reminded of Trell Sylvest. "Since Mr. Carson has offered me a position in his company, I would assume that he would have to check up on an employee." She spoke with all her haughty dignity, and she saw that she was effective at needling the agent.

"He knows there's no such person as Celeste Sanchez."

"I've committed no crimes and I've done nothing wrong. I fail to see where my past would interest you. And what's between my employer and myself is none of your affair."

Hanson laughed softly. "You think you have all the answers. You don't believe Carson is capable of doing anything wrong. What if I told you that he was protecting his mother?"

Celeste felt her body tense. That would go a long way toward explaining many things.

"Look, you can help Mr. Carson."

"I seriously doubt it."

"No, honestly. You can."

Celeste hesitated.

"I can see you'd like to help him. Maybe he is the kind of guy who wouldn't do anything wrong except to protect someone he loves. I personally feel that Mr. Carson has found himself in a jam and doesn't know how to get out. But you could help him. And me. And this country."

Celeste eased her grip on the door. "Show me your badge."

The man eased his identification from his coat pocket and held it out to her. "I want to help Dan, too," he said. "But I can't do it without some help. Your help. What would it hurt to listen to me?"

Celeste considered what he had to say. He'd gone from bullying to reasonable. Maybe he was trying to help Dan. "How could I possibly help?"

"May I come in?" He looked past her into the room.

Celeste felt the cat rubbing against her legs. Familiar stopped at the CIA agent's feet and hissed up at him. Well, she didn't like him either, but if she could help Dan... "Come in," she said, stepping back from the door.

Chapter Ten

Dan had accomplished virtually nothing at the office. Some letters had been signed, calls returned, but his mind was not on business. His normal concentration was gone, and he found himself thinking about Celeste's beautiful eyes, the feel of her skin as his hand slid over it. He desired her, certainly. But what he felt was more than physical attraction. He rubbed the spot on his chest that pained and itched.

He was almost at his car when he noticed the man lurking in the shadows of the office building. The man started walking directly toward him. He wore a badge and a gun, but his hands were hanging at his sides. As he approached, he held them out in front, palms up.

"Dan Carson," he called out.

"Yes." Dan was ready for anything.

"I'm looking for a young woman. Celeste—"

Dan suddenly knew who the man had to be. Kenneth Martin. "You've been impersonating a police officer."

The man shrugged. "I have a job to do. Sometimes it requires bending the truth. I didn't hurt anyone."

"Is it bending the truth or breaking the law?" Dan

asked. For all of his brawn, the man wasn't threatening. It was a good thing, too, since he was armed and Dan was not.

"I don't intend to argue with you, Mr. Carson, I need to speak with Miss Levert."

"Levert?" Dan was surprised. He recognized the name on the ring immediately.

"You know her as Sanchez."

"Her husband's name?"

The man shook his head. "Miss Levert isn't married. But she does need to return home. Right away."

Dan bristled. "I don't think she wants to go home, and she looks old enough to call her own shots."

The man sighed. "You don't understand. I need to speak with her. It's urgent."

Dan wasn't certain what course to take. He had no idea who this man might be in Celeste's life. It crossed his mind that Kenneth Martin might be Celeste's husband, but as Dan scrutinized the man, he seemed to lack the edge of cruelty that would drive a woman to flee for her safety. Whoever this man was, he seemed to know a lot about Celeste. "I'll be glad to deliver a message. She can make up her mind if she wants to see you or not."

The man shook his head. "I know that people have been trying to find her. The men who work for her father or her fiancé aren't always the nicest people." His expression showed his understatement. "I'm not one of those men." He reached slowly into his pocket and withdrew something gold and shiny. He held it out to Dan. "Have you ever seen anything like this?"

Dan recognized the ring instantly. It was a smaller, more feminine version of the ring he'd found in Celeste's room. "Yes, Celeste has something like that."

"If she saw this ring, she'd want to talk to me. I promise you. She has to talk to me."

Dan heard the passion in the man's voice, but he still wasn't certain. "Why should I believe you? As far as I'm concerned, you might be involved in trying to wreck my plane and kill me and Celeste."

"I heard you had some trouble, but I had nothing to do with it. No one in my family would do such a thing. I must insist that you let me speak with Celeste."

Dan didn't like the demand in the man's voice, or the intensity of his gaze. "Or what?"

"Or you may put yourself in a position where Miss Levert will hate you for the rest of her life. Or worse, hate herself."

"What are you talking about?"

"Mrs. Levert, Celeste's mother, is seriously ill. She's been hiding it for several weeks now. I got a call," he patted a cell phone, "not ten minutes ago. She was rushed to the hospital. It's her heart, and there's a chance she may die. I'm sure Celeste will want to see her mother."

Dan could not deny the truth of the man's words. "Okay," he said, motioning to the passenger side of the car. The ring was solid evidence, and if Celeste's mother was as sick as he said, there wasn't time to quibble. "But I'm telling you, if this is a lie or a trick, you'll regret it. You'll wish you'd died as a baby."

"We do not lie about such things in my family," he said. "I'm Celeste's cousin. Kenneth Martin. The ring I carry is her mother's. It has never left her finger since the day she married until she gave it to me as a token to show Celeste the truth of my words."

"Buckle up," Dan said as he headed toward The

Admiralty, his mind racing as fast as the car. At least the mystery of Kenneth Martin was solved, though he'd learned nothing about who had put somadreen in his pilot's coffee.

As they drove to the hotel, Dan cast quick glances at his passenger. Kenneth was dark, but he bore none of the exotic traces that made Celeste so compelling to look at. "You say you're Celeste's cousin?" he asked.

"My mother was a Levert. She chose to leave Lomar and start a new life with her husband." He turned to Dan. "That is why Mrs. Levert knew Celeste would trust me if I could find her."

Dan didn't follow that at all. "Why would that be?"

"Because we are Romani. My mother left her people and settled among the *gadji.* Celeste will trust me because of that."

"The what?"

"The non-Romani people." Kenneth looked at him with raised eyebrows. "You didn't know?"

"Celeste comes from a Gypsy family?" Dan asked. He'd never considered the possibility. Although he knew that Gypsies lived in Texas, they seemed to prefer their own communities. They were a small minority, and he knew almost nothing about them.

"We prefer Roma to Gypsy, but what you're saying is true. She didn't tell you?"

"No," Dan answered slowly. There was obviously a lot Celeste hadn't told him. But he knew the most important issue. "And she's single?"

"She's engaged to marry. But this is her business to tell. I'm not here to make trouble for her. I simply want her to know of Maria's illness.'' He settled back in the seat and stared out the passenger window. ''It would be better for Celeste to tell you these things. You don't know me, but I am also at a disadvantage. I don't know your relationship to my cousin, and I'm not comfortable telling you things she might choose to keep to herself.''

''I understand,'' Dan said, and he did. In fact, he admired Kenneth's restraint. But he was left with his own thoughts. Celeste Levert was Roma. Sanchez had been a good cover name, perfectly reflecting her beautiful skin and eyes. But it hadn't explained the trace of the exotic he'd seen right off the bat. Yes, as he thought about Celeste, it didn't take much imagination to see her as the stereotypical Gypsy beauty. It was an image he knew would be hard to shake.

But there was one question Dan had to ask before they got out of the car. ''Tell me, why is Celeste hiding from her family?'' Dan turned into the drive of the hotel.

''She doesn't want to marry Trell Sylvest.''

''But why run away? Why not just say no to his proposal?'' Dan asked, genuinely puzzled.

Kenneth shot him a glance. ''Her father chose this man. Among our people, the women obey their fathers in the choice of a husband. Especially in Celeste's circumstances.''

''What circumstances?'' Dan felt as if he'd fallen into the plot of a medieval tale.

''Celeste is the only child of Ramone Levert. My uncle is the ruler of our people. Celeste bears the honor and responsibility of that position. Her husband will become the leader, so she must marry wisely, if not for love.''

"That's archaic," Dan said.

"I can't defend it," Kenneth answered. "My mother chose her own way and paid for it by ostracism. It was many years before her family spoke with her. It was a painful choice, but one that she never regretted." As the car stopped he unbuckled his seat belt. "My uncle Ramone is slowly coming around and speaking with her again. It's been hard for him, caught between two worlds."

Dan didn't have an opportunity to respond. Kenneth was already out of the car and headed toward the lobby.

Dan caught up with him and led the way to the suite where he'd left Celeste and Familiar.

AT THE KNOCK on the hotel room door, Celeste turned to Familiar. "We have to do this, to help Dan," she said. Her things had never been unpacked and she had the address that Rick Hanson had given her. Whatever she could do for Dan, she would.

She pulled open the door, expecting to see the bellhop. When she saw Dan, and then her cousin, she stepped back without saying a word.

"Celeste." Kenneth stepped toward her and put his hands on her shoulders. "Are you okay? You look pale."

"I didn't expect to see you here," she answered, glancing at Dan. She was terrified that he would see the intent in her eyes. Rick Hanson had warned her not to let Dan know of her plans. The one complication she didn't need now was a family member trying to take her home—and one brought to her by Dan Carson. How had the two of them ever met?

"I've come to tell you something," Kenneth said, focusing her attention back on his face.

Celeste felt her heart speed up. Kenneth's eyes were worried and sad. She could see that he brought bad news. She firmed her shoulders. "I never thought you would be the messenger sent to convince me to go home. I'm not going, Kenneth. No matter what you say, I won't go back to Lomar and a marriage that I can't think of without getting sick."

"You have to go back," Kenneth said softly. "Not for me. It's Aunt Maria."

Celeste visibly trembled. "What? What's wrong with Mother? I just spoke with her."

"She had an attack. Right after you spoke. I just got a call about half an hour ago. It's her heart. She's in the hospital." Kenneth delivered the news in a gentle voice, his hands supporting her as she slumped.

"Oh, no," Celeste eased down onto the bed. "Is she going to live?" She looked to Dan, as if he might have the answer.

Dan moved to her side and sat beside her, putting an arm around her shoulders. "I'm sorry," he whispered. "I'm sure she'll be fine. We'll get you there as quickly as possible."

"Kenneth, how bad is it?" Celeste asked.

"She's very sick, and she asked me to find you. I was already here, looking for you."

Celeste looked up at her cousin. "This isn't a trick, is it, Kenneth?"

"No," he said. "I wish it were." He reached into the pocket and produced the ring. "Aunt Maria sent this to you so that you would know this wasn't a trick."

Celeste took a look at the ring and began to cry.

She wiped a tear from her cheek, shaking her head. "This is my fault. My running away put too much of a strain on her. She wouldn't be sick if it weren't for me."

Kenneth reached down and lifted his cousin's hand. "This isn't your fault any more than it's Uncle Ramone's for insisting that you marry a man you don't love. This is no one's fault, Celeste. But what must be done is for you to get to Maria without delay." He released her hand and stepped back. "I'm going to the lobby to make arrangements for a flight out. I'll be waiting for you there. In ten minutes?"

"Yes," Celeste whispered. She turned to Dan as Kenneth left the room, softly closing the door behind him.

For the first time she realized that her mother's illness conflicted with the plans she'd made to help Dan. For one spellbound moment she looked into his blue eyes. "What should I do?" she asked.

Dan took both her hands. "I don't know," he said. "Kenneth told me a little about you. I don't fully understand, but I know that you need to see about your mother."

"I'm afraid to go back," Celeste admitted, lowering her face so that he couldn't see her tears. She was scared that if she went to Lomar she wouldn't have the strength to leave again. She was afraid she'd get swept up in duty and obligation and guilt. She was afraid that if she left, the new feelings she could see growing in Dan for her would wither and die. Dan believed his family was cursed. Somehow he'd fallen victim to the idea of disaster touching all he loved— or at least that's what Diana Carson had led her to believe. Dan had never actually admitted such a thing.

Perhaps she was wrong about his feelings for her. Maybe there was nothing there except what she felt.

Dan's voice was soft and strong. "Don't worry about the job. Take care of your mother and the job will be here whenever you can come back," he said. His fingers tightened over hers. "Whatever you do, don't give up your independence out of guilt."

Celeste read his unspoken words. He somehow knew how hard she'd fought to escape her destiny, and now he wondered if she went back if she would ever leave again. Was it because he cared if she returned? Or was this just another act of kindness and generosity?

"I don't want to do this, but I can't abandon my mother."

Dan's grip on her hands tightened. "You're a lot stronger than you think you are." He gave her a smile.

Celeste wanted to touch his face, to let him know that his tenderness gave her strength, yet it was also almost her undoing. It was impossible, ridiculous, but she didn't want to leave Dan Carson. She had no idea what the future might hold for her and him, but she wanted to find out. Going home to Lomar would be like cutting out her heart and leaving it behind. But that wasn't something she could tell him. Not when she was so unsure of his own feelings. Yes, there had been an instant attraction between them. It was still there, as strong as before. But Dan was a handsome man, and no doubt hundreds of women felt the power of his charm. It was best that she return home and tend to her problems without making it worse by mooning over a man she hardly knew.

"I'm sorry," she said. "This isn't your problem, and you've been so very kind."

"I do have a question for you, Celeste."

She heard the seriousness in his voice and her heart began to pound. She had no doubt that Dan had many questions, and she owed him answers. But would it be the question she wanted to hear? "Yes?"

"What about this man you don't want to marry?" Dan asked.

She could not be certain what emotions prompted the question. Dan kept his face expressionless. "You know that I'm Roma," she said slowly.

"Kenneth told me. He explained a little."

"He told you that I'm my father's only child?"

Dan nodded. His gaze was fastened on hers.

"I know it's hard for an outsider to understand, but within our clan there are responsibilities. There are rules and laws that help us maintain our identity."

"And the arrangement of marriage to a man you don't love is a small sacrifice?"

She heard the disbelief in Dan's voice and she knew it would be difficult to make him understand. "That's my father's view. And my mother's." She lifted her chin. "I would have accepted my role, except the man my father selected is not a man of honor."

She could see that Dan struggled with her words. But she knew he could understand if he tried. She believed his heart was big enough, and she saw that she was right.

"You would marry a man you didn't love for the sake of your people?"

"I would," she said without hesitation. "But Trell

Sylvest is not the man my father believes him to be. Trell has fooled my father.''

"But not you?'' Dan's hand grazed her cheek, and Celeste had to fight the urge to reach over and touch him.

"I've known him since we were children. He wishes to marry me only because of the position he'll achieve. Even that would be acceptable, except that he won't protect my family, my clan. I defy my father as much for my people as for myself.''

"And how did you end up in Dallas?'' Dan asked. "I know you don't have time for these questions, but…''

"I studied investing. Against my father's wishes. I had a knack for math in school, and I was lucky. My aunt Lorrain, Kenneth's mother, encouraged me when she could. She helped me with correspondence courses. I taught myself until I thought I knew enough and then I ran. I was lucky to get a job with Stevens and Lynch.''

"Lucky? They don't hire someone because she's lucky. You obviously have a talent.''

Celeste shrugged.

"What will you do about your fiancé?'' Dan asked.

"I'll have to deal with that when I get home.'' Celeste took a deep breath. "I'll be okay.'' She looked at him and felt as if she were saying goodbye forever. "Will you really keep my job for me?'' That was not what she wanted to ask, but it was the only legitimate thing she could request.

"For as long as it takes,'' he said.

"You're not even angry that I let you believe I had an abusive husband?'' She bit her bottom lip. "I wanted to tell you the truth, but I didn't want to involve you in the mess. And I was afraid you'd find it all unbelievable—that I was running from a marriage, from a man my father chose.'' She blinked back tears at the idea of Trell Sylvest. How was it possible that he might yet prove to be her fate? "It does sound like something out of a book.''

"Meow!"

They both looked at the black cat.

"What about him?'' Dan asked. "You could leave him with me. That way I'll know you'll come back after your mother recovers.''

"Maybe I should. I know you'll take good care of him.'' Celeste hated the idea of leaving Familiar. But it might be better for the cat.

"Meow!" Familiar said, putting a paw on each of their legs.

Everything was happening too fast. Celeste had hardly been able to absorb the request made of her by the CIA agent. Now the news of her mother's illness had turned her world around like a kaleidoscope. And she wasn't imagining that Dan was showing more than just a courteous interest in her problems. He didn't want her to leave. He was afraid she wouldn't come back.

She wanted to bury her face against his chest and cry, but that wouldn't solve a thing. And she had no right to even consider it. Since she'd stepped into his life, she'd brought only confusion and turmoil.

"Meow!" Familiar dug in with his claws.

"Ouch." Celeste bent down to draw him into her lap. "I don't think he wants me to leave him.''

As if to emphasize her words, Familiar reached over and put a paw on Dan. "Meow.''

Dan shook his head. "I don't know what's wrong

with me. I'll fly you to Lomar. I can see you safely there, and Familiar won't have to endure a commercial flight.''

Celeste couldn't believe the offer. It would make everything so much easier. And it would also give her time to make the arrangements that Rick Hanson had requested of her. If her mother was okay, she could still make it back to Dallas to meet Jess Harper. She might yet be able to repay Dan Carson for his many kindnesses to her.

''That would be wonderful,'' she said. ''We should tell Kenneth. I'm sure he'll be relieved.''

''I'll call Kip and see that the plane's ready.'' Dan snapped his fingers. ''There's no need. He took care of that, and I'll fly you myself.''

Celeste gathered Familiar in her arms. ''I'm ready,'' she said.

Dan picked up her luggage. ''Let's go.''

Celeste opened the door and halted so abruptly that Dan almost ran into her.

''What?'' he asked.

Celeste didn't speak but she pointed to the door knob. Swinging on a string hooked around the knob was the gold ring that belonged to Maria Levert. Beneath it was a large stain that could only be blood.

Chapter Eleven

Even as she climbed the steps into the plane, Celeste had tremendous misgivings. Kenneth had disappeared without a trace. And Dan was incredibly tight-lipped about what he thought had happened to her cousin.

They had notified hotel security and the police. A search was in progress. Several of the hotel staff had seen Kenneth in the lobby using the telephone, and a quick check at the airport had confirmed the flight reservations he'd made. Dan canceled them and left word with Kip to conduct his own search for the missing man.

Celeste had called home and spoken with her father. His relief at hearing her voice had caused her great suffering, but Ramone Levert had not yielded an inch. He had told Celeste that if she came home to see her mother then she should come willing to accept her duty.

Knowing that it would do no good to argue with her father, Celeste had said only that she would be there as quickly as possible. She would deal with her father later—when her mother was better.

Celeste settled into one of the plush leather seats with Familiar in her arms. ''Dan, I could just as easily take a commercial flight,'' she said. Kenneth's disappearance had greatly unnerved her. She didn't want Dan stepping deeper into her family troubles.

"I wouldn't dream of it,'' Dan answered. "If this Trell Sylvest is behind your cousin's abduction, he's going to be one very sorry man. I'll make certain of that.''

Celeste didn't doubt that Dan would make his threat a reality. His face looked as if it were carved in stone.

"I have a car waiting for us at the nearest airport to Lomar. We'll be at your mother's side in a matter of hours,'' Dan reassured her.

Celeste felt her emotions rise and knew that the vicious cycle of hope and despair had started again. It felt as if she'd climbed onboard the biggest roller coaster in the world. It was all a slow climb up and then a sickening drop to terror and fear. There was no question that she had to confront her family. Running away had not been the way to handle the situation. She would sit down with her father and make him understand, after she made sure her mother was going to be okay and Kenneth was found.

"Get ready for takeoff,'' Dan called back to her as he taxied the plane onto the runway.

She admired his ability with the craft. They were airborne with hardly a quiver, and she unbuckled her seat belt and went to the cockpit.

"Dan, do you really think Kenneth is okay?'' Dan's reassurances were the only thing that had kept her sane. She had come to rely on his judgment, and on him. But the blood belied Dan's assertions that Kenneth was probably okay. The blood and the ring, left as a message to her. The trouble was that she didn't know what the message meant.

"I can't imagine that anyone would harm him," Dan said. "He convinced you to go home. That should please your father and Mr. Sylvest."

She noticed his difficulty in saying Trell's name, and she had to admit that it thrilled her. "Would you like something to drink?" she asked, wanting only to put her hands on his shoulders. The impulse was foolish, and she knew she'd never yield to it, but it was what she wanted.

"No coffee," Dan said, finally giving her his irresistible grin. "How's the cat?"

She looked back to see that Familiar was sound asleep. "I think he likes to travel," she said. "Odd, because most cats hate it."

"One thing we know for certain, Familiar isn't like most cats."

"I think he'd agree with that. He seems at home anywhere." And I'm at home nowhere, she mentally added. The irony of her plight struck her. She was flying back to a situation she'd found intolerable with a man she barely knew yet longed to kiss. She fought against the urge to lean down and brush her lips against Dan's neck. "I'll get us a soft drink," she said, hurrying away. She had to put some distance between herself and Dan. She had to.

DAN BROUGHT THE plane down in one long, smooth landing. Celeste had taken her seat and read a book for the brief trip. He could tell she was withdrawing from him, emotionally as well as physically. He understood that she had no other choice, and he could not offer her another option. She had been honest with him, but he had not told her the truth of his past. Not the complete truth.

As he'd listened to her speak of her family, he'd known that he loved her. She was a woman who took her bonds seriously, a woman who fought hard for the chance to do what she felt was right. And not just for herself, for her family and her community. These were values he could not help but respect. And Dan found that respect was the key that unlocked the emotions he'd kept under such tight control. He'd been able to walk away from other beautiful women. Celeste was different. He admired her courage, and ultimately, her willingness to face her own worst fears.

As soon as the plane taxied to a stop, he walked back to her. He could see that she'd been crying, but she was making a supreme effort not to show it. Familiar was purring in her lap, alert and watching everything. Dan wondered what actually went through the cat's head. He recalled the luggage incident. Familiar had gotten him out of a pinch. He really was an extraordinary cat.

"Meow." Familiar looked up at him and one eye winked shut.

Dan chuckled, leaning over to scratch his head. "I swear he's smarter than I am."

"Meow," Familiar agreed.

Even Celeste chuckled. At last she unbuckled her seat belt.

Dan knew she dreaded this. She'd telephoned her family from the Houston airport. They knew she was arriving, and she'd made it clear she wanted to handle this alone. "When I get back to Houston, I'll check with the police about your cousin," he reassured her. He didn't want to let her go.

"What will I ever tell my aunt and uncle?"

"The truth," Dan said gently. "If someone has taken Kenneth against his wishes, chances are that he'll end up right here in Lomar."

"That's true," Celeste said. "It's the only reason I agreed to leave Houston without him. I suspect this is Trell's work." She said the name with such anger that Dan put a hand on her shoulder.

"If it is, I'm sure you'll make him regret it."

"Count on it," she agreed. She put the cat aside and rose to her feet.

Dan wanted to tell her that he'd be back for her. He wanted to reassure her that he would be waiting. But he couldn't offer his love until he was certain that he would not harm her. Not only because of the curse but also because of the situation he was in with Rick Hanson and the oil deal.

His time was running out. He had to be back in Houston, and then he wanted to get to the ranch before anyone else so that he could prepare for the meeting. And he wanted to talk to Jess. Whatever the CIA agent had said, Dan had come to a decision. Celeste had been the motivation. He understood the complicated issues of lying to protect, and lying to manipulate. Celeste had hidden her background because it was almost unbelievable. In his world an abusive husband was much more understandable than an arranged marriage. Her fabrications had harmed no one.

He couldn't say the same for his lies. He'd drawn Jess Harper into a deal that could cost his old friend money, if not things of more value. Reputation. Safety.

At first Dan had thought he would flat out refuse to participate in the sting. But after watching Celeste and her obvious concern for her community, Dan felt that he couldn't turn his back on a request from his own country. Even if it came from someone as thoroughly despicable as Rick Hanson. He would go through with the plan. On his own terms.

Dan had decided that he was going to tell Jess the truth. That he was involved in a sting operation, and that Jess had been drawn in as a middleman. If Jess wanted to help him, then that was good. If he didn't, Dan would set up the meeting without involving Jess. Dan knew that it was the only way he could live with the end results, no matter what they were. And once he had the oil problem resolved, then he would turn his attention to the Carson Curse. He had seen Celeste's skepticism about the curse. And her reaction had made him think. No one in the Carson family had made any attempt to validate the curse. And it wouldn't be hard. Dan simply had to find out the name of the woman who had allegedly cursed the Carson family and look her up. Once they were face-to-face, Dan was certain that the issue of a curse would be resolved.

All he needed was time.

Picking up the cat, Celeste started toward the exit. Familiar leaped from her arms and darted into the cockpit.

"Come on, Familiar," Celeste urged. But the cat backed away from her. She shook her head. "He acts like he doesn't want to come with me."

Dan didn't understand the cat's contradictory behavior, but he knew that Celeste needed to see about her mother. "Why don't you leave him here?" Dan suggested. "I know you feel responsible for him, but he'll be fine."

"I don't understand it," Celeste said, finally giving up on the cat. She disembarked with Dan behind her. He felt her shock as she stopped on the steps. He looked past her and saw the two men lined at the side of the runway. The older man was obviously Celeste's father. He was handsome, very tall and dignified. And beside him was a younger man with finely chiseled features and longish hair pulled back into a clasp at his neck. His shoulders bulged with muscle and his hips were lean. He had the look of a man who spent hours honing his physical appearance. Both men wore exquisitely cut suits, and they watched Celeste, completely ignoring him.

Dan couldn't resist. He put a hand on the small of Celeste's back, a gesture of support and ownership. "We can turn around and go back to Houston," he said softly.

"You can. I can't," she answered, stepping forward.

Dan followed close behind. He'd intended to put her in a car and see her on the way to the hospital. She hadn't asked him to go with her, but as Dan took in the men, he had a sense of foreboding. He didn't want to leave Celeste.

"Father," Celeste said as she approached the men. She pointedly ignored the young man. "This is a friend of mine, Dan Carson. When we learned that Mother was ill, Dan offered to fly me here. Dan, this is my father, Ramone Levert."

Dan felt the older man's eyes move over him in disapproval. The younger man radiated anger. Dan extended his hand, which Mr. Levert refused. He saw Celeste color and turn away. "I'm going to see Mother."

Ramone's voice stopped her. "When you left Lomar without regard to your duties or your family, she ceased to be your mother."

Celeste faltered, and Dan almost rushed to her side. But he held back, knowing that to do so would imply that she was too weak to stand on her own. He saw a grim look of satisfaction on the younger man's face and only rigid self-control kept him from smashing his fist into Trell's nose. That and the knowledge that it wouldn't help Celeste in the long run.

"Be that as it may, I'm going to see her." Celeste was defiant, and her dark eyes flashed a warning. Dan had seen her worried, reticent and determined. Now she was magnificent as her eyes snapped with a dare that anyone get in her way.

"Before you see Maria, you will agree to the formal announcement of your engagement to Trell." Ramone's long, elegant hand waved between the two of them. "Trell has grounds to renounce the engagement because of your actions. You have chosen to abandon your people and live among the foreigners. But he has agreed to forgive you."

Celeste's fists tightened at her side. "Father, you know that I love you, but I didn't come home to marry Trell. I came to see Mother. Trell's forgiveness is of no importance to me, because I can't forgive him for being an opportunistic, greedy man."

Dan wanted to applaud, but he could see that her response had angered both men. Ramone Levert's face was suffused with blood.

"You're not my daughter. You're not Roma. You've been tainted by the outsiders." He turned and started to walk away.

"Be that as it may, I'm going to see Mother. Then

I'm leaving." Celeste brushed a tear of anger from her cheek.

Trell stepped toward Celeste, his eyes narrowed in anger. "Your mother won't see you. She knows her place, and she knows that she must obey the laws. You're an outcast, Celeste. Everyone you grew up with will turn their backs on you whenever you approach."

Trell's hand shot out and grabbed her shoulder. "You've given up everything you ever had. This isn't necessary, Celeste. You haven't even given me a chance."

Dan's hand came down on Trell's arm with such force that Trell stumbled backward, then hugged his wrist to his chest.

"Don't ever touch her again," Dan said with deadly intent. "Not ever. Don't even think about it."

"Where's Kenneth?" Celeste asked, stepping between the men and confronting Trell.

"Your cousin?" Trell asked. "How would I know where he is? He lives with his mother, who also abandoned our people."

"He'd better be okay," Celeste said angrily. "You got what you wanted. I'm here."

Trell stared at her. "Your father has no children. The people will vote on a new ruler, and he will wear the ring that you stole. It isn't yours to keep."

Celeste's hand rose, then fell back to her side. "I may not rule my people, but I'll make sure you never do it, either," she vowed. She put her hand on Dan's arm. "Can we go to the hospital now?"

"Right this minute," he replied, leading her toward the small airport terminal. Her hand on his arm had been confirmation that she didn't want him to leave her. And it was the only signal he needed.

CELESTE KEPT HER back straight and her shoulders squared as they walked toward the terminal. As Dan had said, a rental car was waiting for them. She hadn't anticipated a greeting committee at the airport. But maybe it was just as well that she'd gotten it over with. The lines were clearly drawn now. She would make sure her mother was getting better, and then she would leave Lomar forever. There was no going back.

Dan's presence at her side gave her a sense of comfort, and as he handed her into the car, she allowed herself to think what life would be like with him always beside her. It wouldn't replace what she was giving up. Nothing would. But Dan would bring his own dimension to her life.

"Are you okay?" he asked as he took the directions she gave him.

"I think so." She shook her head. "I'm sorry you had to see that. My father isn't a cruel man, but he holds to the old ways tighter every year. I think he's afraid that if he doesn't, we'll begin to slip into the culture around us and be absorbed."

"Would that be such a terrible thing?" Dan asked.

It was a question Celeste had asked herself. "Not for me. I've already made that choice. For others, though, it would be intolerable. Throughout history the Roma have maintained their own unique culture. Many of the elders feel my generation is throwing it away. They think we don't value our heritage. But what we want is a chance to be a part of a bigger culture." She thought Dan might be bored by her explanation, but when she looked at him she saw he was paying close attention.

"I have to agree with your assessment of Mr. Sylvest," Dan said. "He doesn't strike me as a man who cares who he steps on as long as he gets ahead."

"My father is blind to that." Celeste sighed. "Trell feeds Father's need to isolate us. He goads my father into thinking that even a small change is dangerous. I think if Trell were out of the picture, Father would be more reasonable."

"And your mother?" Dan asked.

Celeste understood his fear. "I don't know," she answered softly. "Mother did send for me. I can't believe she'd turn me aside, but…" She couldn't finish. If her father ruled that she was impure because of her contact with outsiders, then her mother would have to deny her. It was the law.

Dan parked in the shade of an evergreen tree and they walked toward the small hospital.

"We could have her transferred to Dallas," Dan suggested. "She'd have better facilities."

"Let me talk with her."

"Shall I wait out here in the lobby?" Dan asked.

Celeste thought for a moment. "No," she said. "You've been so kind to fly me here. I'd like for her to meet you, to know that the entire world outside our town isn't mean or bad."

"Okay," Dan said as they went to the information desk and found her room number.

At the hospital room door, Celeste tapped lightly. When she heard her mother's voice telling her to enter, Celeste put a hand on Dan's shoulder. "Give me a minute alone with her," she said.

Dan nodded and stepped back. Celeste wanted to

place her hand against his face, to tell him how much it meant to her that he was beside her. But she only gave him a faint smile as she entered the hospital room.

The sight of her mother, so tiny-looking in the hospital bed, startled Celeste. Maria Levert looked pale against the white hospital sheets, and Celeste couldn't help the small cry of concern. "Mother!" she said, rushing to the bed. Maria was pale, but her eyes were bright and her hair neatly combed.

"Celeste." Maria smiled at her and reached out to run a hand over her hair. "I knew you'd come home. It was just an attack, but Ramone insisted that I come to the hospital."

"I was afraid you wouldn't see me," Celeste said.

Maria nodded. "That's why I sent the ring. Your father has threatened to make you an outcast."

"I came as soon as Kenneth told me you were sick." Celeste reached into her pocket and drew out the ring her cousin had shown her. She had no intention of worrying her mother about Kenneth's strange disappearance. She was certain Trell had done something to him, and now that his usefulness was over, Trell would release him.

Celeste took the ring and slid it back on her mother's finger. "There," she whispered. "Now it's back where it belongs."

"And the other ring? The one your father gave you to seal the engagement with Trell?" Maria's eyes drew together in a frown.

"It's safe," Celeste reassured her.

"You must obey your father," Maria said softly, reaching out to lift Celeste's chin so that they stared eye to eye.

"I can't," Celeste responded, lifting her mother's hand to her face and holding it there. "I can't."

"I know how hard it will be for you. *At first.* But it will get better. Ramone would never select a husband who wouldn't treat you with respect. Maybe one day you'll grow to love him as I did your father."

Celeste shook her head. "Another man, perhaps. But not Trell. And besides," she kissed her mother's hand, "I've already found someone to love."

"What?" Maria struggled to sit up higher in the bed. "What did you say?"

"I wasn't sure until today, but I know now. This trip here—it showed me what kind of man Dan really is. I've met the man I love, Mother. He doesn't know it yet, but I do."

"Someone from Dallas?" Maria asked. "You've only been gone for three months. Surely you haven't fallen in love in such a short time."

"Not Dallas. Houston. But it doesn't make any difference where he's from."

"Who is he?" Maria asked.

"He's outside the door right now. Should I tell him to come in?" Celeste kissed her mother's hand again and released it. "He doesn't know what's in my heart, and I'm not certain what he feels for me. But I couldn't hide it from you. I want you to know that I'll be happy. He's a wonderful man. You'll see." Celeste went to the door. "Dan, would you come and meet my mother?"

She took his hand and led him into the room. She was looking at his face when she saw it change. The warm, expectant smile dropped away and she saw consternation. She whirled around to her mother.

Maria Levert sat bolt upright in the bed, her right hand pointing at Dan.

"Get out of this room," she said, her voice almost a hiss.

"Mother?" Celeste started toward her.

"No! It can't be." Maria's voice rose. "Get him out of here. Get out of this room this instant. And you go with him. Now!"

Chapter Twelve

I think if I had a Hollywood agent, I could make some money today. Home Alone *was a popular movie. What about* Alone on a Jet? *That's my story, and I stayed behind for a very good reason. Several of them.*

First of all, hospital food makes me ill. Even the idea of it. Secondly, Dan needs someone to watch this birdie. He seems to have forgotten that an intruder got onboard long enough to drug the coffee supply. What's to stop someone from doing something worse? So I decided to stay and make sure that the Goddess, Dan and I have safe passage back to Houston.

Of course, I could be wasting my valuable time. But then I did notice some smoked salmon in the galley, and I think there were some prawns in butter. Why is it that businessmen always have such delicacies stored in the larders of their planes and they never seem to eat them?

I suppose that Dan has been a little busy flying the plane. And trying not to moon over Celeste. It's so plain to me that those two are head over heels. But they both act like they're afraid of getting burned.

And what a whirlwind of activity has occurred. I

can't decide if Dan or Celeste is at the vortex. There's definitely something strange going on with Dan. Then again, I've been fascinated by Celeste's revelations. The daughter of a Gypsy king! That's royalty in my book.

But what a sad life she's had. As a cat who descended from a long heritage of alley cats, it was hard for me to adapt to living the life of an adored and pampered house cat. Change is very difficult. But the world changes and the only option is adaptation. And, a TO such as myself can clearly see how the feline has adapted to a world growing more and more perilous for four-legged creatures. We have moved from the yard into the house, we've set up our domains with bipeds as our willing slaves. Where we once ruled the jungles, we now reign supreme in the den.

On one hand, I can understand tradition and heritage and culture and how important they are to a people who have roamed the world for centuries. But I also understand that Celeste is a beautiful young woman with a major talent. It isn't right that she should be punished because she wants to have a job and her own life.

And as for that Trell Sylvest! What can I say about a man who can see his own reflection in the tips of his polished shoes? I can see why she ran away from him. Besides, Celeste was made for Dan.

Watching them together, ah, it just does an old cat's heart good. From the first moment their eyes met, they felt it. In the maze, when Dan came rushing after Ayla, I knew it. These two are destined to be together. No matter what Roma laws they break or how many people think it's wrong, I know this is their destiny.

The problem is making sure they understand they belong together. It's a proven fact that humans aren't all that smart when it comes to romantic matters. I've made this observation before.

Well, it's up to me. I rather enjoy the role of Cupid. And I'm one heckuva shot with the old arrow in the heart.

But wait a minute. There's someone at the door of the plane. Let me climb up in this little nook and see if I can—yes, indeed. Who should it be but the Spoiler. I wonder what Mr. Sylvest is doing here.

He's breaking in. No shock there. He didn't strike me as the type who hesitates at breaking the law. And he's doing it with some style, though. Yep, the door is opening and here he comes. Now, should I attack or wait and see what he's up to?

I think I'll wait and see. He's not expecting a sleek black kitty guard, so the element of surprise will be with me. He's going through Celeste's luggage. I'll bet he's looking for the ring. But I happen to know it's on a chain around her neck, so there's nothing for him to find. I think it's time for me to take action.

I noticed the emergency alarm pull near the cockpit. I'm not exactly certain what it'll do, but I'm willing to bet it'll get airport security over here in a big hurry.

Okay, so I'm going to suffer a few bruises, this is necessary. One mighty lunge at the switch. Eureka! It sounds like a fog horn. And Trell Sylvest looks as if he's stuck his finger in a 220-volt outlet. He's headed for the exit, and now's my chance.

One black fur ball, ready to launch. Contact! One

paw swiping down the face and he's screaming and out the door.

And here comes the security team. Now I'd better find a hiding place and let them do their work. I am a little sleepy. I think I'll curl up in the luggage rack over Celeste's seat. It's dark, it's cozy, and it's just my size. There's nothing like a bit of a nap after a hard day's work.

DAN SAW THE security vans at his plane and he felt Celeste tense. The scene in the hospital room with her mother had badly upset her. So much so that she wasn't even talking about it. He knew she'd been embarrassed by her mother's behavior. Maria Levert had acted insane. He'd never had anyone look at him as if he were Satan incarnate. But Celeste's mother had acted as if he were the embodiment of evil. It had surprised him and greatly upset Celeste. And now something had happened to the plane.

He pulled up and got out, showing identification as he began to ask the chief of security what had happened.

"The alert on the plane went off and we've checked her from top to bottom. There was no one on the plane. The only thing disturbed was some luggage."

Dan looked over at Celeste as she waited, huddled in the car seat. It was her bags. He hadn't brought any. He saw her mouth tighten into a line and guessed that her thoughts had gone to the same place as his. Trell Sylvest was looking for the ring he coveted.

Well, it was typical. He'd had just about enough of Lomar and the bizarre behavior of the people there. It would be better for Celeste if she left and never looked back. Easier said than done, he knew, but getting on the plane and flying away was a good start. And time was of the essence.

He walked around to the car. "I'll check the engine, but then we'll be ready to go."

When Celeste looked up at him, her eyes were empty. The sparkle and life seemed to have drained away. Dan was so concerned that he reached down to her and grasped her hand. "What is it?"

"I'm staying here," she said in a voice that had no inflection.

"Celeste?" Dan couldn't believe it.

"I have to."

"No, you don't. There's nothing to keep you from going right back to Houston. You can start a life there, one with sanity and sense."

Celeste's smile was a shadow of her old one. "I can see where none of this makes sense to you. But it is my past, and before I can have a future, I have to put this in order."

"What can you do?"

"I want to know why my mother reacted as she did."

"It was clear that her reaction was to me," Dan said as gently as he could. "From what I've gathered, she was upset because I'm not Roma."

"No." Celeste shook her head slowly. "It's more than that. I told her about you and she wasn't that upset. It was only when she saw you."

Dan didn't understand it, but he also didn't know Maria Levert. Celeste's mother wasn't his primary interest, though. "I can't leave you here," he said, meaning it. "I don't trust Trell Sylvest, and I'm not certain your family will come to your aid now."

"No one will hurt me," she said. She squeezed Dan's hand. "There's something I must do. And I must do it alone," she said, forestalling any attempt Dan might make to stay.

Dan knelt beside the car. "I can't leave you, Celeste."

She reached out and touched his face, her palm caressing his jaw. "You have to."

Dan rose, and he pulled her gently out of the car seat. "Let's go on the plane where we can have some privacy to talk," he said.

"I want to get Familiar," she agreed. "If he'll come with me."

"If I have to leave you here, I won't leave you without Familiar to take care of you," Dan said, and he wasn't joking.

As soon as they were onboard, the black cat jumped from the luggage compartment and began weaving between Celeste's feet. She stooped down and gathered him into her arms. "He seems fine now," she said.

Dan looked at the cat and then walked over to the security alert mechanism. "I know it's going to sound crazy, but I think Familiar stayed on the plane because he suspected someone would come onboard."

Celeste's eyebrows rose. "I think you're right." She kissed the top of Familiar's head and earned a major purr. "Even Familiar agrees."

Dan checked the control panel and the operation of the instruments while Celeste made sure nothing had been taken from her bags. As he worked, Dan kept glancing at Celeste. His reluctance to leave her was like a physical pain in his chest. He rubbed the place where the marble arrow had stabbed him and felt a

tiny bit of relief. He considered locking the door of
the plane and taking off with her in tow, but he realized that the one thing she didn't need in her life
was another man wresting control of it.

She'd fought long and hard to be able to make her
own choices, and though he didn't agree with this
one, he had to step back and let her make it.

"Meow."

He looked down to see the cat staring into his eyes.
"You don't think I should leave her, do you?"

The cat's head moved left and right.

Dan sighed as he scooped Familiar into his arms.
"I know I shouldn't. But I have to. And I have to go
soon, so it'll be up to you to take care of her."

"Meow," Familiar agreed, hopping to the floor.

When it was apparent that nothing had been done
to the plane, Dan returned to the passenger area. Celeste had her bags ready to go, and she stood there,
waiting. Dan had never seen anyone so brave.

Before he could stop himself or even think about
what the consequences might be, he gathered her into
his arms and held her.

CELESTE CLOSED her eyes and yielded to the comfort
of Dan's body. The intense sexual charge jolted
through her, and she did nothing to fight it. There was
no fight left in her. And beyond that sensation of desire and need, she found something more. Dan's arms
enclosed her and for the first time in a long, long
while she felt loved and safe.

Perhaps it was all in her own heart and mind. Dan
was the kind of man who offered comfort to those in
need because he could. It did not mean anything more
than that. But it didn't matter. Celeste knew that she

loved him. And in the oddest way, it was enough, for the moment. She had wondered if she was odd or unable to love because she'd never found that connection with any of the men she knew. With Dan, it was there. Solid, strong, undeniable. And even if nothing came of it, Celeste knew that she was capable of a love complete and total.

"I won't argue with you," Dan said softly into her hair. He held her close, and his heart beat in her ear. "It goes against everything I know and feel to leave you. But my needs are secondary here."

Celeste pressed lightly against his chest, enough so that she could look up and into the blue eyes that drew her like magic. In all of her life, no one had ever put her needs first. Not that she hadn't been loved and cherished. But her needs had been assigned and approved.

This was the independence she'd fought so hard to attain, and she hadn't even understood what it really was until now. Until Dan gave it to her.

"I thought when I left my home that I was escaping an unwanted marriage and finding a job and a career." She swallowed, almost overwhelmed by emotion but determined to continue. "Those were important things. But what I was really seeking was my *self,* an acceptance of who and what I am. And I think I found that, but I also found something much more important."

Dan brushed his fingers under her jaw. "What would that be, Celeste?"

"I found a man I could love." Celeste's hands moved up his chest and circled his neck. "I love you, Dan. And I thank you for the gift of this love." She put a finger on his lips when he tried to speak. "Don't feel that you have to respond." Her smile was wry. "One thing I've learned is that love is a gift, and unless it's freely given, it's worthless. I give you this and I expect nothing in return."

"Not even a kiss?" Dan asked.

Celeste's smile widened. "Maybe just one."

His lips came down to meet hers. Celeste was breathless at the tenderness of the kiss. What Dan hadn't said in words, his mouth conveyed to her.

And then the kiss deepened, and all thought and reason fled. There was nothing but sensation and a growing need to feel Dan's skin against her, to know his touch.

DAN SLID his hands along her back, sculpting the lean curves of her body. No woman had ever felt so right. Celeste Levert had walked into his life with the drama of a hurricane, and she had blown away all of his control.

And perhaps it was time.

He couldn't go on any longer without feeling something for someone. He didn't want to live that way. He wanted to spend hours and days and weeks kissing Celeste. He wanted to tell her that the gift of her love was returned.

But before he did that, he wanted to kiss her just a little longer. His hand moved down her sleek back, pulling her closer against him. She responded with a moan that was like fire in his blood.

The plane was not the place he would have chosen for a romantic encounter, but he conceded that the desire that arced between him and Celeste was too powerful to resist. It didn't matter where they were. All that mattered was that they were together.

"Celeste," he whispered, moving her toward the plushly carpeted aisle.

Her answer was the movement of her hands down to his waist. She tugged his shirt free and ran her hands under it, her fingers exploring and turning his own blood to liquid fire.

"Are you sure?" he asked. If she insisted on staying in Lomar, he would have to leave her. And he wanted no second thoughts, no regrets. She was too important to him.

"Quit talking," she answered, beginning to unbutton his shirt. "I've never been more sure of anything in my life." She shook her head as she looked up and into his eyes. "Are you sure?"

He laughed softly. "I've never been more sure of what I wanted and less sure of the consequences," he admitted. "I can't stand having my heart broken."

"Of all of the things I wanted to experience away from Lomar and my family, breaking the heart of a kind and wonderful man wasn't on my agenda."

"Do you promise?" Dan asked it lightly, but he wasn't completely kidding. He had not risked his heart in a long time. With Celeste, he knew that once he'd made love with her there would be no turning back. He could not bear to lose her as his lover, his love.

"I promise that once I get things straight with my family and do the things I need to do, I'll return to Houston. To you."

Dan had forgotten how such simple words could change his life. "I'll hold you to that," he said.

"Good," Celeste said, and in her eyes was the twinkle of life that he loved so much. "So stop talking and help me out of this dress."

She turned slightly so that he could find the zipper, and in a moment the dress fell around her ankles. With a graceful step, she was out of it. Together they sank to the carpet, and Dan allowed his hands to move over her perfect skin. He leaned down and covered her lips in a kiss that went from tender to passionate.

On the soft carpet they made love.

CELESTE SNUGGLED closer against Dan's chest, knowing that each precious second would be imprinted in her mind. Their lovemaking had been passionate and intense, and in the aftermath, she listened to Dan's regular breathing and allowed the sense of happiness to sink deep into her bones.

This was what it meant to love a man. This was joy. And she had been right not to settle for less.

At that thought, she felt a pang of sadness for her parents. Maria Levert claimed that she had grown to love her husband, and from all Celeste had seen between them, it was true. There seemed to be a deep, steadfast bond between her parents. But there had been a time when Maria Arleotta had loved another, someone unacceptable to her family.

Perhaps that was why Maria had reacted so strangely when Dan entered the hospital room. It was possible that it brought back to Maria the hardships she had endured when she'd tried to break away from the strict rules of her people.

There was a difference, though. Celeste knew she would never return. She had a career and a future. And she had Dan. If she could only make her mother understand the bond that was between her and Dan.

A bond they had just made stronger with an intimacy that made her dizzy if she thought about it.

Dan's arms came around her and she felt his lips at her ear. Even such a small touch started another cycle of desire. But there wasn't time. She had to get to Dallas and take care of the matter she'd promised Rick Hanson she would do.

"Dan," she whispered, kissing his chin and his jaw.

"Ummm," he answered, lifting her so that she shifted on top of him.

Celeste shook her head so that her hair teased and danced over his face and the ring she wore on a chain around her neck tapped his chin. She was delighted with the smile it brought to his lips. "I love touching you and feeling your hands on me," she said, laughing at his response. "But I have to go."

"I know," Dan said, but his grip on her waist tightened. "I hate leaving you."

"It's only for a short time. I'll be with you in Houston before you have time to miss me," she said, lifting herself off him.

"I already miss you," he said, catching her and pulling her back down. "Maybe we can just stay here. We can send Familiar out to forage for us, bringing in food and whatever he finds. I'll bet he can be quite self-sufficient."

Celeste laughed at the image and sat up. She reached for her dress and began to pull it over her head when there was a loud commotion outside the plane.

Celeste stood up and handed Dan his clothes. Familiar came at a gallop out of the cockpit and stationed himself at the door.

"What now?" Dan asked, slipping quickly into his clothes.

Celeste went to the window and looked out. "It's Trell and my father. My goodness, Trell's face looks exactly like—"

"A cat clawed the dickens out of him," Dan stated, leaning against her. "I think we know who our intruder was."

"And he's here to get this ring." She pulled it from around her neck and dropped it in Dan's hand. "Keep it for me, Dan. I'll get it from you when I get back to Houston."

"Are you sure?" Dan asked. He was looking at the two determined men staring at the plane. Several security officers had surrounded them, but Dan knew by the expression on their faces that not even an army would deter Ramone Levert and Trell Sylvest.

"I'm sure." She turned so that she could kiss his cheek. "I may return it to my father, after he's had time to think about what he's doing. I don't claim the rights of the ring, or the responsibility. I just want him to think carefully before he gives it to Trell, or anyone else. I don't want him to make a mistake because he's angry or disappointed with me."

"And they'll leave you alone about it?" Dan asked. He didn't want to leave Celeste with the possibility that Trell Sylvest would be dogging her and breaking into her room to search through her things. Or worse yet, trying to touch her.

"They will." She nodded. "My father may be angry with me, but he loves me. And he'd never allow anyone to hurt me. I'm willing to stake my life on that."

She said it with conviction, and she only hoped that Dan wouldn't be able to tell that she was bluffing.

Chapter Thirteen

The jet lifted off the runway like a graceful bird, and Celeste turned to face the two men. She had left Dan's plane, walked across the tarmac and entered the airport, knowing they would follow her. And they had. She could have gotten in the rental car and driven away, but she knew it would do no good. Trell would follow her, springing out at her when she least expected him. He loved the advantage of surprise, even when it wasn't necessary.

The best way to deal with him was directly. "Father, I—"

"Give the ring to Trell," Ramone Levert said slowly. "Then it would be best if you leave. There's nothing here in Lomar for you any longer."

The words were like a knife in her heart, but she refused to show her father how much he hurt her. "The ring is mine. By birthright."

"You've given up that birthright."

"I have not. I've simply decided not to marry a man who is…" She turned to Trell. "I don't love. A man who would kidnap my cousin. Where's Kenneth? I know you had him taken from The Admiralty. Release him, Trell. I'm leaving Lomar and I'm not going to interfere with your plans. But let Kenneth go.''

Trell's broad shoulders shrugged. ''I don't know what you're talking about.''

Celeste rolled her eyes. ''Lie if you wish. Just let him go.'' She turned to her father. ''I'm going to speak with Mother and then I'm leaving. I'll return the ring in several months, once you've had time to cool off.'' She shook her head. ''When you realize what kind of man Trell is, you'll find someone more worthy to give the ring to.''

Trell stepped closer to her. ''You've judged me without cause. You made a judgment long ago, without considering the circumstances. People can change, Celeste.''

Celeste looked at her father. ''I've made my choice and I won't change my mind.''

''This isn't your choice to make,'' Ramone said with anger.

''I'm making it my choice. This is the result.'' She checked back her emotions. ''I need to see Mother.''

''Don't bother going to the hospital,'' Ramone said. ''Your mother will not see you.''

Celeste saw that her father looked at her as if she were a stranger. She would not give them the satisfaction of her tears. She simply turned away and began the long walk to the car. All the way she could feel their gazes on her. She felt her father's despair and Trell's delight and satisfaction. And she realized that she'd played perfectly into his hands. Now he had everything he wanted without the burden of a wife who would not obey him.

Well, this round had gone to Trell, but it wasn't over.

She got in the car where Familiar gave her a rough licking on her arm. Thank goodness for the cat. And Dan. She looked toward the west where his plane was no longer visible in the night sky. He was on his way home, but she knew he would have been here for her if she had allowed it. That was the thing that kept her strong.

She decided against going to the hospital. Even if Maria wanted to see her, Celeste knew her mother would be hard-pressed to go against Ramone's directives. It would be better if she went to Dallas and found Jess Harper. She had to deliver the important message Rick Hanson had entrusted to her.

But first she needed sleep. She was exhausted. She climbed back into the car and drove toward a small hotel, her body tired and her mind whirring.

The trip to Lomar had been worthwhile because she now knew her mother was distraught and upset, but she was not gravely ill. The tension of the past months had taken a toll, but she would be fine.

And in a few weeks, or months, when things had calmed down, Celeste would return and talk with her parents. She would give back the ring and allow her father to do as he wished. She could only hope that a little time would soften her father's heart and allow him to see reason. Perhaps in that time Trell would overplay the hand he held and show her father his true colors.

She felt a twinge of guilt for not telling Dan what her plans were. He'd assumed she would remain in Lomar, and she'd done nothing to contradict that assumption. Because the CIA agent had made it clear that her mission was to be kept secret. So, she would pay a visit to Jess Harper and then catch a flight to Houston.

Jess Harper. She focused on her task. The CIA agent had told her that Jess was an old friend of Dan's and that he and Dan were working together on a very important deal. Rick explained that the CIA had been watching Jess for several months and they were concerned that Dan might be drawn into something illegal.

Celeste had been reluctant to step into Dan's business, but Rick had explained that Dan was caught in a terrible position. He did not believe that his old friend had become a crook, and therefore he wouldn't abandon Jess in the middle of what he assumed was a legitimate deal. Celeste's job was to deliver a simple message. It was an assignment she willingly accepted, though she wasn't certain exactly how she could protect Dan. He was far more experienced than she was at spotting a bad deal, but Rick had insisted that this would be vital to Dan's future. And it seemed such a little thing to ask of her after all that Dan had done.

She checked into the motel and found her room. Without undressing, she fell into bed and slept, Familiar curled at her side.

THE MORNING dawned, bright and sunny. As the miles spun away beneath the wheels of the rental car, carrying her back to Dallas, Celeste found her thoughts wandering back to Dan. He was the most remarkable man she'd ever met. And she'd told him that she loved him. Her face flushed hot at the memory. It was a bold move for a young woman who'd just left the protection of her family. But whatever happened, she would never regret loving him. This was the feeling that poets wrote about and battles had been fought over. She smiled at her own fancy. But the feeling was still there. And she suspected that Dan felt the same way. He hadn't said as much, but he had shown her his heart.

Although she'd never regret making love with Dan, Celeste realized that it had complicated things. Working at Carson Dynamics would be a problem. And she wasn't certain about Diana Carson. Dan's mother had gone to great pains to tell her about a family curse—one that had negatively affected Dan and his siblings in love. Celeste couldn't help but wonder at the motivation behind such a revelation. Diana had essentially stepped into Dan's personal space in a way that Celeste couldn't ignore. But why? Did Diana actually believe in such a curse?

The solution to that was so simple Celeste almost laughed out loud as she thought of it. Of course it would take time—for Maria to accept Dan as her son-in-law. But once Maria met him and got to know him, she would love Dan. So if the Carson family actually believed in such a curse, Celeste would simply ask her mother to stage some type of curse removal. Or to get one of the older residents of Lomar. Maybe Mrs. Esthers. She was the town storyteller, the one who kept the old myths and legends going. She would be perfect for a little ceremony, and she was thespian enough to make it seem real.

If Diana Carson was superstitious enough to believe in a curse to begin with, then a curse removal would be just the ticket. After a few months, Celeste was sure Maria would cooperate in the plan. In time, even her father would come around. She had disappointed them, but the bitterness would fade. They were good people and they loved her.

All in all, once a few minor matters were put into perspective, the future looked good. Almost too good to be true. She had a career ahead of her, a really good one with the chance to grow and learn and experience new things. But better than that, she had Dan. Her heart told her that she hadn't stumbled into a casual fling. This was for real, forever.

She was almost surprised to find herself in the thick traffic of a big city. She'd been so absorbed in her own thoughts that the drive had seemed to take only a few minutes. The cityscape of Dallas grew larger and larger in the windshield of her car, and she followed Agent Hanson's directions perfectly. The traffic absorbed her attention until she found the building and pulled into the parking garage. Jess Harper wasn't the only person working on a Saturday—the lot was half-full.

She looked over at the cat. "I hate to leave you in a parked car," she said, "but this isn't really a place for a cat. Not even a handsome black one." She scratched under his chin. "I'll be back soon." As she slid out of the car seat, she didn't notice that Familiar slithered along the floorboard and slipped out the door.

He followed right on her heels as she entered the elevator, and he was a silent shadow as she entered the business complex. As she moved to the receptionist's desk, Familiar scooted behind a potted plant.

Celeste gave her name and stood at the desk waiting. She wondered if Jess Harper would even see her. Many businessmen wouldn't take a call from someone without a formal appointment, especially on a weekend. To her surprise there was the sound of rapid footsteps and she turned to find a sandy-haired man in his early thirties headed directly toward her.

"Miss Sanchez?" he asked.

Since Celeste had told Dan the truth about her last name, she felt awkward with the one she'd assumed. She smiled and held out her hand. "Yes, and you must be Mr. Harper."

He ignored her outstretched hand. "I've been expecting you," he said brusquely. "Follow me."

Celeste didn't know what to make of his behavior, or his knowing she was coming, but she fell into step behind him and went into the office. He closed the door with unnecessary force and turned on her.

"I don't know what you're trying to pull, but it won't work. I'm not the kind of man who yields to blackmail, and I'm certain if Dan had any idea what you were up to, he'd have you run out of the state on a rail."

Celeste closely examined his face as he talked. Jess Harper was not pretending to be mad. He was angry. But why? And who had told him to expect her visit?

"There's some confusion here," she said carefully.

"I don't think so." He went to a desk and picked up an envelope. He dumped the contents on his desk. "You're playing Dan for a fool and you're trying to draw me into something illegal. Well, I won't be a party to this and once Dan understands what you're up to, I'm sure he'll send you packing."

Celeste walked slowly to the desk and looked at the contents of the envelope. Photographs were scattered across the desk. They showed her at the Sweetheart Ball in Dallas talking with two men, one dressed as the Phantom of the Opera, complete with mask, and one as Napoleon. She remembered them vaguely, businessmen who worked part-time in Dallas and around the world. She had been mildly flattered by their attention.

At her questioning look Jess laughed. "Don't play innocent with me. You know those men."

"I don't," Celeste said.

Jess walked around her. "You're good. Very good. I can see why Dan fell for you. The perfect opposite to Shawna in appearance, yet a woman with acute business sense. You're exactly what the doctor ordered. I wonder how long it took them to find you and put you into position. And then I had to invite Dan to meet me at that ball where the whole little scheme could be put into motion. I could kick myself, lady, but at least my part in this was an honest mistake."

Celeste couldn't begin to decipher what Jess Harper was talking about. She felt as if she'd stepped off a cliff and was in free fall.

"Who are those men?" she asked. In the photo, it looked as if they were acquainted. But the masks hid the men's eyes.

"You know them. They work for a major oil importer."

"I don't know them," Celeste said, making sure that Jess Harper was looking directly at her. "I'd only been in Dallas for three months when I went to the Sweetheart Ball. I really didn't know anyone there except my colleagues from Stevens and Lynch."

Jess pointed a finger at her chest. "You are one convincing liar, I'll give you that."

"I'm not lying. Who told you these things about me?" she asked, puzzled. "When you answer that question, you should ask yourself why I'm here and who told me about you.''

Those simple words had a marked effect on Jess. He walked around to his desk and slowly sank into the leather chair. He waved her toward one of the wing chairs. ''Maybe you'd better sit down,'' he said. ''You've just given me something to gnaw on for a moment.'' He picked up the photos and looked at them again.

Celeste, too, picked up several of the pictures. It seemed as if someone had followed her around the entire evening, snapping a shot every time she spoke with anyone. She didn't remember two-thirds of the people she chatted with, but it had been a loud party and there had been hundreds of people there. But someone had been photographing her the entire evening. The idea of it made her skin crawl.

''Tell me what you know about me,'' Celeste said. She eased back into her chair.

''That you lied about who you are, that you played on Dan's sympathies to get him to hire you so that you could infiltrate his business. That you came here today to plant something on me so that if the deal went wrong I'd take the fall.''

Celeste leaned forward. ''What would I plant?'' She held up her purse, dropping it on the desk. ''Examine it. See what's there.''

Jess didn't wait for a second invitation. He opened it and dumped the contents on the desk. Pushing aside lipstick, compact, brush and billfold, he found a small black leather case. As he picked it up he looked over the desk at her.

''Business cards,'' Celeste said.

He opened the case and fanned them out. His eyebrows drew together in a frown and he lifted one card out. Dropping the others he glared at her. "So innocent. I almost fell for it."

"What?" Celeste felt her stomach sink. She'd been completely set up. "What is it?"

He handed her the card. She flipped it over and saw the telephone number scribbled on the back with the odd name *Midnight River* beside it. Even though she didn't know what it meant, she knew it was something sinister.

"You won't believe me when I tell you that I don't know what this means and I don't know how it came to be in my possession."

"No, I won't." Jess reached into his desk drawer. "What I do know is that I have a meeting to attend and I can't leave you here. So, I suppose you're coming with me." He pulled his hand out and the barrel of a gun was pointed directly at her chest.

Celeste swallowed. There was no arguing with the gun. "I left my cat in the car in the parking garage."

"Then you'd better pray that you don't cause any trouble. If this meeting goes the way it's supposed to, then you'll be back here in less than forty-eight hours."

Celeste stood up. "I can't leave an animal shut up in a car without food or water for two days."

Jess picked up her car keys and tossed them in the air, catching them. "I'll have my receptionist take care of the cat. But get this straight right now. We're walking out of here together, and you're going to be very convincing in the attitude that you want to be with me. Is that clear?"

Celeste looked at the gun. "It's clear."

"Don't make me hurt you," Jess said as he put the gun in his jacket pocket and took her arm.

HERE COMES THE Goddess, along with Dan's old college friend. But Celeste looks a little strained. She's walking as if she had a ramrod up her spine. Uh-oh. Something's not right. So, Jess is making arrangements with the receptionist to get me out of the car and Celeste isn't even putting up an argument about it. No, this isn't good.

I'll just tag along and see where we're all headed. I get the feeling that Celeste is going to need my help. My instincts back at the Sweetheart Ball were absolutely on target. This woman is in trouble, and only I can save her.

DAN CHECKED HIS flight plan. Shortly after leaving the small Lomar airport he'd changed his course and headed for San Antonio and the ranch. It was time for the meeting he'd set up with Phil Norris. He was concerned. Jess Harper hadn't returned any of his calls, but then Jess could be anywhere in Texas, or the world.

He remembered his father's old saying, "In for a penny, in for a pound." That was exactly how he felt. All he wanted was to get the meeting over with and put it behind him.

Celeste Levert was his future. And what a future it was going to be. He felt a little foolish that he hadn't told her he loved her. Maybe it was superstitious foolishness. But he wasn't going to say the words until he had cleared up all possibilities of the tragic past returning.

Of course, he wasn't certain that saying the words

had anything to do with it. Perhaps just loving Celeste was enough.

But he wouldn't think that way. She was in her home with her family—as troubled as they were. He had to believe she was capable of taking care of herself. It was the most important gift he could give her, other than his love.

As he approached the San Antonio airport he called the tower and made preparations to land. It would take him an hour or so to drive to the ranch.

The landing was smooth as glass and he got out of the plane and into the sun of a perfect February day. Even though this was a business trip he didn't want to make, he felt a sense of pleasure at going to the ranch. He'd always loved the hill country and the solitude of the old ranch his father had bought and refurbished.

He checked his bag to make sure the gun he'd packed was still there, and then he headed for the car rental where a vehicle was waiting.

As he headed northwest, he thought of the work that remained for him at Carson Dynamics. He'd be back at the office soon. Thank goodness he'd avoided his mother and gotten away without having to explain this trip to her.

He covered the distance at a fast clip and turned off the interstate to pick up the old county road that led to the ranch. It had been called the Pebble Creek Ranch before Jake Carson bought it, and they'd left the name.

Dan saw the old arched wooden sign that marked the entrance. Cattle grazed on either side of the drive, and Dan caught sight of three deer as they bounded over the rolling pasture.

The drive went up a steep hill, then swung down to the small creek that gave the property its name. Large stones, washed smooth and white by the brisk current, created a cobblestone effect on either side of the creek. Dan slowed long enough for one happy thought of the picnic he'd love to take Celeste on beside the creek. There were so many things he wanted to share with her.

He headed up another hill to the house. As he crested the top and got his first view of the house, he slowed. The door of the huge barn to his right swung slightly. Normally the doors were kept latched. He drove to the barn and got out of the car. He entered the barn slowly, allowing time for his eyes to adjust to the darkness. At first he didn't believe what he saw, but as he stared, he realized it was true.

He walked slowly to the man who was tied to the barn post, almost hidden by rows of hay. Blood coated the man's chest, and Dan feared that he was dead.

As he drew closer, the man moaned, and Dan hurried forward. Gently he lifted the man's head where it hung on his chest. He said nothing as he recognized the battered face of Kenneth Martin.

"Run," Kenneth whispered through lips that had been severely beaten. "Run. They're gone, but they'll be back soon."

Chapter Fourteen

Celeste twisted at the ropes that bound her wrists, but the knots were firm—as they had been ever since they'd gotten off the small prop plane at the grassy airstrip outside Banderos. She was not amused when Jess cast a look at her and grinned.

"I know you're used to traveling in better style with Dan, but I can't afford it. But you do get a free travelogue. This is the cowboy capital of the world," he said as he waved at the small town they were passing through.

"Maybe when this is over you can get a job as a tour guide—in prison," Celeste said angrily. Her wrists were raw and her back ached from the position she was in. "There's no need to keep me tied. What am I going to do, throw myself out of a moving vehicle?"

"My inclination is to untie you. That's exactly why you're tied. You must be something to have slipped past Dan's defenses. He's a very cautious man, especially where women are concerned."

Celeste was torn. Jess had opened a door she wanted to go through, but she didn't want to go with him. More than anything—except her freedom—she wanted to know about Dan's past. But Jess Harper was insane and mean. Was there any point in listening to anything he had to say? She looked out the window at the rolling Texas hill country. She had nothing better to do than listen. She was a prisoner in the car until Jess got her to wherever they were going.

And then? She couldn't allow herself to think about that. She had no real idea what she'd stumbled into. Jess was carrying a gun, and that boded ill for her. That thought was enough to send her back to the more comforting thoughts of Dan.

"Dan's mother told me his bride was killed in an automobile accident. Do you know what happened?"

Jess glanced sharply at her. "You sound like you might actually be interested. Now I've got to figure out why."

"I've already tried to explain to you who I am and what I was doing in your office. You don't believe me, so it doesn't matter what I tell you. Humor me and tell me your version of the truth about Dan and his...fiancée."

"Shawna Wright was something else," Jess said, staring at the road. "Everyone in our class was in love with her, but it was Dan who won her heart."

Celeste watched him closely. For such a tough man, Jess gave away far more than he dreamed. She had a sudden memory of Mrs. Esthers, the old woman in her town who had a booming business as a fortune-teller. Mrs. Esthers had a gift, Celeste knew, but it was not in seeing the future. She was able to read human nature and determine what her clients truly wanted and what they feared.

In explaining what she did, Mrs. Esthers had told Celeste that it was a fact of human nature that most people could achieve what they wanted—if they believed they could. She read her clients' hopes and dreams and helped them believe that true love or money or health was possible, if they began to take the necessary steps to attain those things. In believing, in taking action, they made their dreams come true.

Watching Jess, Celeste understood that he, too, had been in love with Shawna Wright. And she saw something else. Jess had kept his feelings to himself. He had not vied for Shawna's attentions, because of his great love for his friend.

"Tell me about Shawna," Celeste said softly.

"She was beautiful, smart and full of life. That's about it in a nutshell. She always had energy to do something more, a new idea, a better way of doing things. And she never had to take the credit. She was generous to a fault."

Celeste digested Jess's description and realized that Dan could not have loved a woman who was less than wonderful. "She was killed on the way to the church?"

"It was terrible. We were all in the back of the church waiting. Dan was pacing the floor, and the rest of the groomsmen just stood around. We could hear the clock ticking. She was five minutes late, then ten, then twenty. It was terrible. And Dan wouldn't talk. We didn't know what to do. Shawna was never late. It was one of her virtues. She was on time for everything. We all knew something had happened, but we thought maybe the car had stalled or something had gone wrong with her dress. You know, typical stuff that goes wrong at the worst possible time. At least that's what we were saying to Dan. But deep down I knew it was tragic."

"Was it one of Dan's cars?" Celeste asked the question, wondering what prompted her to even think of it.

Jess's reaction was the same. His eyes narrowed as he glanced at her. "What are you getting at?"

"I don't know," Celeste admitted. "Please, tell me what you remember."

"It was a rented limo. Carson Dynamics was a thriving business, but it wasn't what it is now. It was only after Shawna's death that Dan simply threw himself into the business. That's what he did, twenty-four, seven. He worked. And in the process, he built a financial empire. But it wasn't like that ten years ago. Carson Dynamics was a good living, but Dan didn't have limos and planes like he does now."

"Okay," Celeste said, feeling her way through her own thoughts and feelings. "What happened at the church?"

"After half an hour Dan's mother came and told him that it was obvious Shawna wasn't going to appear. Diana Carson looked like she'd aged a decade. It was terrible. She and Dan just looked at each other, and you could see that Dan's heart was breaking. They were both thinking it was that stupid curse thing, that Shawna had gotten cold feet on the marriage and simply decided to stand Dan up at the altar."

"But it was so much worse," Celeste said, overwhelmed at the horrible scene Jess was laying out before her.

"A lot of the guests got up and left, but Dan refused to leave. He said he knew Shawna wouldn't do such a terrible thing. She would have at least sent a messenger or something."

"What did you believe?" Celeste asked.

"I didn't know what to think. Shawna loved Dan. I knew that. This marriage wasn't a game to her. And even if she'd changed her mind, this wasn't the way she'd handle it. Shawna was cool when it came to business. She was the most ambitious person I'd ever met. I think it was because she came from a really poor background. But she had a tender heart and there is no way in hell she would have done such a thing to Dan.

"Anyway, I had a bad feeling, and then the policemen came in through the doors of the church." Jess's voice grew very soft as he slipped back to that moment in time. "There were two of them, and they walked down the aisle together. I had this terrible feeling that something awful was coming. They went straight up to Dan as if they knew who he was and asked him if he knew Shawna Wright. And then they said they had bad news, that she'd been involved in an accident and had been killed."

For a long moment there was only silence in the car. Celeste wanted to reach out and touch Jess's arm, but her hands were bound and she was his prisoner. It wasn't exactly a scenario where she could offer sympathy. Still, she couldn't deny his pain. After ten years, he still suffered. What must it be like for Dan? Shawna Wright was a woman who touched people deeply. Strangely enough, she felt no jealousy or threat as far as her feelings for Dan were concerned. Each love was a different road, a different experience. She had learned that from her mother. Only fools attempted to relive the past through different lovers, and Celeste firmly believed Dan was no fool. He was ready to experience a new love with her. She knew it even if he hadn't come straight out and said as much.

"I'm truly sorry," Celeste said. "I can see that you loved her."

Jess didn't bother denying it. "From the first moment I saw her. But she was Dan's. There was no doubt about that. She never even saw me or any of the other guys. She came into the business school and went to Dan like he was a homing device." He sighed. "I didn't begrudge him her love. You couldn't. They were just meant for each other and I accepted that."

Jess slammed the steering wheel with his hand. "It's that damn curse. Dan didn't believe it, and neither did I. We made jokes about it. Even Shawna." He hit the steering wheel again. "The day before the wedding we were laughing about it. It just makes me sick to think about it all."

Celeste didn't question the feeling that came to her. She'd been sent to Jess Harper's office to deliver a message. When she arrived, she found that he was waiting for her and that he'd been warned that she intended to plant something on him. It was clear to her that she and Jess both were being manipulated like chess pieces. She had doubted Jess at first, thinking perhaps that he intended to use Dan for his own personal gain. She didn't believe that any longer, and she knew that before they got to Pebble Creek Ranch, she had to make Jess understand that they were allies.

"Jess, I'm in love with Dan." Celeste waited for the reaction her words would have. At first Jess acted as if he hadn't heard her.

"Right," he finally said, glancing over at her as he slowed the car. "I'm in the middle of a very tricky negotiation which wouldn't bear close federal scrutiny. I get a phone call from someone who warns me I'm about to be set up. And now you manipulate me into talking about the past and declare your love for Dan.'' He rolled his eyes. ''I must be the biggest chump in the world. I let you get to me.''

''Who called you?'' Celeste asked. ''Was it Rick Hanson with the CIA?'' She had a bad feeling about the agent.

Jess's jaw clenched and unclenched. ''The call was anonymous. I have the feeling you're playing me like a fiddle, and I don't like it.''

''I love Dan,'' Celeste said. ''I'm not Shawna, and I can't replace her. I don't intend to try. But I love him. And I don't believe in the Carson curse.''

Jess pulled the car onto a side road, the tires slewing slightly in the loose gravel. He drove up a hill and finally pulled to a stop where they were off the roadway and secluded.

''What do you know about the Carson Curse? Who are you?'' he demanded.

''I don't know anything about that particular curse, but I do know that the only power a curse has is that it can begin to control the people who believe in it.''

''You have no idea. Dan's entire family—''

''Has suffered romantic setbacks. So, who hasn't? You loved Shawna, but you didn't win her. Does that mean you're cursed and will never find true love? Or that every time you love you'll lose her to your best friend?''

''Who are you?'' Jess repeated.

''My real name is Celeste Levert. My story is complicated, but I would never do anything to hurt Dan or any of his friends.''

"Why should I believe you?" Jess asked.

"Because your heart tells you to," Celeste said simply. She held out her hands. "I met Dan at the Sweetheart Ball, as your picture showed. There was a man there who later attacked me in the gardens outside the house. Dan must have noticed that I was fleeing from the man because he followed and rescued me. And then he offered me a job to help me get out of Dallas and build a new life."

"That sounds like Dan," Jess agreed. "He's always trying to help people."

"I had my own set of problems dealing with my family in Lomar. Believe me when I tell you that I wasn't aware that Dan was having any difficulties until I found a CIA agent in my hotel room yesterday."

"You said something about the CIA," Jess said.

"Rick Hanson. He nearly frightened me to death, but he said he came to warn me that Dan was in big trouble. He asked me to meet with you and give you the message I tried to give you earlier."

Jess reached for the keys. "I'm not going to listen to anymore," he said. "I don't trust you."

Celeste knew she had to reach him. "That's not true, Jess. You don't trust yourself."

She saw his face tighten in anger and then relax. "Tell me the message."

Celeste held out her hands. "Untie me first."

"Forget it," he said, reaching to turn the car on again.

"Jess, I think that Dan's life may be in danger. If we don't work together on this, he may be hurt."

He turned angrily to her. "What are you, some kind of voodoo woman? You don't believe in the

Carson Curse but you somehow know we have to work together or Dan will suffer?''

Celeste reached her hands out to him. "Untie me. I don't believe in curses, not any of them. And I know we have to work together because we both love Dan. The only other person I know involved in this is the CIA agent, and I don't believe he loves Dan. So between my choices, I pick you."

"I don't know that you love Dan, though," Jess answered stubbornly. "Prove it."

"How?"

"Tell me something about him that would make me believe."

Celeste laughed softly. "He won't say that he loves me because he's afraid of the curse."

He eyed her critically. "Maybe he doesn't love you."

"Untie me, drive to a telephone and call him. Ask him. I think he'll tell you the truth."

Jess drummed his fingers on the console.

"Look, you have the gun, just untie the ropes." Celeste was staring directly at him when she saw his eyes widen and he leaped up in the seat, banging his legs against the steering wheel.

Kicking and jerking, Jess thrashed to the side, hitting the console so hard that it drove the wind out of him. She saw her chance and reached into his coat pocket and grasped the gun. Though her hands were tied she was able to hold it with her finger on the trigger.

"Sit up and hold very still," Celeste said, pointing the gun right at him. She was still puzzled at his behavior. It was almost as if he'd had a seizure. "What's wrong with you?"

Jess grew very still before he slowly straightened up. He leaned down and began to rub his legs. When he pulled his hand up it was covered in blood. "What the hell?" he asked. "There's something under the seat."

Celeste felt an intense relief. It didn't seem possible, but... "Kitty, kitty," she called softly.

She was answered by a slow meow.

"I think you'd better untie me now," she said, wiggling the gun slightly. "If you don't, my attack cat will have to have another go at your legs."

"Cat? How did a cat get in this car?"

Celeste could see that he didn't really want to believe her. She was having a hard time taking in the fact that Familiar had been able to trail them without ever giving his presence away. He'd gone from the parking garage to the office to the car to the plane and now here. He was truly an amazing animal.

"He's a highly trained guard cat," Celeste answered with more than a hint of mischief. She was so delighted that the cat was safe she couldn't help smiling. And once again he had saved her. "Come on out, Familiar."

There was a scrabbling in the back seat and Celeste glanced back to see Familiar leap into the seat and begin to lick a paw.

"How did you manage all of this?" she asked the cat.

Familiar gave her one long, golden look and then returned to licking a paw.

"That's something I'd like to know," Jess said sourly. "I thought you said he was locked in the parking garage."

Slowly she lowered the gun. "Please untie me," she said as she put the gun down on the seat.

"You actually think I will?" Jess asked.

"I think you'd better, or Familiar will jump on your head and you'll be sorry you believed an unidentified caller and took me hostage."

Jess reached across and began to undo the knot. "I don't know why I believe you, but I do." As soon as the rope was undone, he sat back. "And I guess you'd better tell me the message you came to deliver. I can't promise that I'll act on what you say, but the cat is very convincing."

"Rick Hanson told me to say, 'The past is never dead. Protect Carson from his ghosts.'" She raised her eyebrows. "So, what does that mean?"

"I don't have a clue," Jess said. His brow furrowed as he thought. "'The past is never dead.' That's true for everyone. I can't imagine why you'd have to deliver that message personally. Why didn't he just call me up and tell me this? Or pay me a visit himself? This doesn't make a bit of sense." He cast a suspicious look at her as he retrieved the weapon.

"I gave you a show of faith. You now have the gun," she stated. "I'm telling you the truth because I'm worried about Dan."

"Okay," Jess agreed. "I'll think about this dark message and what possible ghosts might come back to haunt Dan. Maybe some business deal that went bad and the investors are out for revenge. That's about all it could be," he said as he started the car and headed back for the main road.

THANK GOODNESS. I thought I was going to suffocate under the car seat. I didn't want to give my posi-

tion away because the element of surprise is so crucial in a tight situation. Now, though, I can sit on the seat and view the passing countryside. Looks a bit familiar, not to make a pun. Rolling hills, live oaks, scrub cedar, this is the general territory where San Antonio Safari used to exist. You know, I just love it when bad things happen to bad people. And those big game hunters deserved what they got.

But what am I going to do with Jess Harper and the goddess? They seem to have come to some terms, but I don't know that it will last. I can't believe she gave the gun back! When all this is over I'll have to have a long talk with this young woman about men and guns and trust.

So, the car is in gear and we're off to the ranch. I wonder if they have a ranch cook. That plane Jess flew us in didn't have so much as a can of tuna. But at least it was easy enough to sneak onto. I went right past his leg and he never even noticed me. I have a bad feeling that we're going to need all the sneakiness we can muster in the next few hours.

I'm fascinated by Rick Hanson's message for Jess. Ghosts from the past. It is unusual, and something that could easily have been delivered on the phone because it has no hard information in it. Or it appears not to. It's more of a vague threat. But the humans are missing a very important point here. If Hanson intended for Celeste to deliver her message, then who planted the business card on her? Was it Hanson? And why would he sabotage his own messenger? Who else could it be?

So many questions, so few answers. I think I'll curl up in the sunny window for a little nap. A rested kitty

*is a kitty ready for trouble. They're going to need me
sooner than they think.*

*I wonder how far we are from this ranch. I need a
little yard exercise. I've been cooped up in hotels or
planes for the past few days. It'll be good to round
up a few doggies. Not the slobbering beasties that
bark, but the gentle moo-cow kind. Doggy is cowboy
lingo for cattle, you know.*

Ah, I love the west.

Chapter Fifteen

Dan half dragged, half carried Kenneth into the ranch house and eased him down on a sofa. Dan was no medic, but he could see that Kenneth had been severely beaten. He tried to ascertain the extent of the injuries, determining that no major bones seemed broken. Whoever had delivered the beating had been expert at dealing pain and suffering without causing death.

"Who did this?" Dan asked.

Kenneth shook his head. "I didn't know them."

"What happened?"

"I was headed back to the hotel room when I was grabbed from behind. I tried to escape, but they started beating me. They didn't even ask any questions. I came to here. I don't even know where I am, or where they went."

Dan wasn't so sure Kenneth's attackers were gone, but he didn't say anything. He felt in his coat pocket for the gun. The cold steel gave him a bit of comfort, though he'd never thought he would find himself in a position to shoot anyone.

"Were the men who abducted you sent by Celeste's family?" Dan asked. Dan thought he knew the answer to that question—Celeste's family would never have brought Kenneth to Pebble Creek Ranch. But he asked in the hope that it might trigger a memory in Kenneth's mind.

Kenneth shook his head. "I don't know. I got a pretty good look at them. I didn't know them, but that doesn't mean a thing." Kenneth tried to raise his head up. "Where's Celeste? Is she okay?"

"She's in Lomar," Dan said. "She's fine. Or at least as fine as she can be with her family so mad at her."

"She's a lot tougher than she looks," Kenneth said. "She's like my mother, which would make Uncle Ramone mad if he heard me say it. But Celeste is strong enough to make a new life. She'll be okay."

"Then why did you come to talk to her?" Dan asked.

Kenneth hesitated. "My mother suffered because she was cut off from her family. It's an old tradition, and one that must be changed, but when a Roma, or Gypsy as you call them, leaves the family community and chooses another life, they're ostracized. My mother was treated as if she were dead. I was hoping Celeste could figure out a way to bridge the gap. I know Uncle Ramone and Aunt Maria love her more than anything in the world. I wanted her to talk to them, to try to make them understand."

"Perhaps in time they will," Dan said. He didn't say it, but he intended to make the Leverts accept Celeste's decision. He didn't know how he intended to do it, but he knew he would somehow succeed. He would not allow her to suffer. Somehow, he would make her family understand her need to be independent.

He got up and paced the room. "We have a completely different problem facing us, and soon. I'm supposed to meet some men here for a business deal. These are dangerous men. And I'm afraid you're caught in the middle."

Kenneth struggled up to a sitting position. "What's going on?"

"It's something I got involved in, and I mean to settle it here. I don't want you getting killed in the process."

"You mean you don't think I can handle it." Kenneth got to his feet.

Dan considered the other man's determination. "Okay," he said, walking across the den to the gun rack. He selected a high-powered hunting rifle and the proper bullets and handed them both to Kenneth. "The barn's the best vantage point on the place. If I come outside with my hands in the air, shoot whoever is behind me."

"Shoot to kill?"

Dan thought about it. "Wound them if you can disable them. These are dangerous men. Ruthless, as I'm afraid you've already found out. They know you're here, and probably know I've arrived as well. There's only one way out of this, and I intend to come out at the end alive."

Though his lips were badly swollen, Kenneth smiled. "I like that attitude." He took the rifle and Dan led him through the house to the back door, which had the shortest distance of open space to the barn.

"Be careful," Dan urged him.

"That's a warning you should give the other side," Kenneth said as he darted toward the barn.

Dan watched him go and could only hope that he'd made the right decision. In the barn, Kenneth would be relatively safe. Unless things went terribly wrong.

The sound of tires on the gravel drive sent Dan hurrying to the front of the house. On the way he drew his gun out of his pocket and checked the chamber to make sure it was loaded. It was a precaution that told him how serious he was.

Where in the hell were Rick Hanson and the CIA agents he'd promised to have on the scene? So far everything Hanson had promised had been a lie. Dan was no longer surprised at the agent's failure to deliver.

The car coming up the drive was not one Dan knew, and he held his breath until he saw that the driver was a woman. He didn't believe it when his mother parked in front of the house and stepped out of the rental car.

Pushing the door open, he stepped out onto the porch. "What are you doing here?"

At the level of frustration in his voice, Diana lifted an eyebrow. "I told you I might come to the ranch. Surely these Neanderthal businessmen won't object to a woman cooking a meal for them. After all, my place is in the kitchen and that's where I'll stay."

"Mother," Dan said, walking forward. He grasped her arm and pressed her back to the car. "Get in and drive."

"Dan," Diana Carson shook herself free. "I don't know who you think you are, but don't ever talk to me in that tone again."

"It isn't safe here." Dan looked down the driveway. He was expecting Norris at any moment. Where the hell was Jess?

"What's going on?" Diana Carson's dark eyes seemed to burn with a hot light. "What are you up to? You'd better tell me. I'm not going anywhere."

Dan saw the determination in her face. He knew he wouldn't be able to make her leave, at least not without an explanation. By then it would be too dangerous for her to try to drive away. She might meet the crooks as they were coming up the drive. "Come inside," he said, putting urgency in his words by taking her arm.

"This had better be good," Diana replied.

Dan didn't hold back. "Remember the deal you cut for oil off the *Midnight River?*" He felt her stiffen. "You were set up."

"I got it at a damn good price," Diana said. "We'll make a killing on that oil." She bit her lip and looked down. "It was a good deal for us, Dan. I had to take a chance. The profit margin—" She shook her head. "I was in deep."

"We might get killed. It wasn't Louisiana oil. It's from the Middle East. You've been pulled into the middle of a mess, and I'm here at the ranch to straighten it out."

He saw his mother deflate. She sat back on the arm of the sofa. Her posture never changed a fraction, but it was as if someone had knocked the air out of her.

"I tried to explain to the CIA that you were innocent. They know it's true, but they demanded that I help set up a sting. I'm meeting Phil Norris here in a matter of moments."

Diana looked around. "This is an ambush? Dan, it's too dangerous. These men are callous."

Dan had grave doubts that Rick Hanson would follow up with his end of the bargain. He was supposed to be on the scene with CIA sharpshooters to take Norris into custody. But Dan had seen no sign of federal agents or anyone else. It looked as if it were going to be up to him. "You have to go out to the barn and stay put," Dan said. "There's a man out there with a rifle. He'll protect you."

"And you?" Diana asked, standing suddenly. "Who's here to protect you?"

"I'll be fine."

"You're the bait because of my mistake." Diana's back became ramrod rigid. "I won't leave you here." She pointed to the gun rack. "I can shoot. Your father taught me to use every gun there, and I was a pretty fair marksman."

"It's one thing to shoot at a paper target, another to aim at a man," Dan reminded her gently. "Go to the barn. Promise me you'll stay there with Kenneth. If I don't have to worry about you, I'll be safer."

Diana reached out and put her hand on Dan's shoulder. "I'm so sorry about this," she said. "I never should have…"

Dan shook his head. "Stay in the barn. We'll talk about this once it's over. But go now. Before it's too late."

"Give me one of those guns," Diana said. "The 410. That way my aim doesn't have to be too accurate."

Dan handed her the small shotgun and a box of shells and watched as she hurried toward the barn. There was time for nothing else as a red car blasted up the driveway. Dan ducked back into the house and hurried to the front to catch a view of the new arrival. It had to be Norris. He was surprised to discover that the car contained only one man and a woman bundled in a big coat, a scarf and sunglasses.

As they headed toward the ranch house, Dan felt his stomach knot. The man was very familiar. He stared as the man turned to the woman, pushed her and pressed the gun barrel into her ribs. Dan knew him. He was Joshua Brando, formerly CEO of one of the biggest Texas banks and a former professor at the university he'd attended. Dan well remembered the night Brando had come up to him and Jess and Shawna and offered Shawna a job. She'd turned him down. And a good thing, too. But Dan knew he would never have suspected the prestigious banker of involvement in illegal oil deals.

The woman stumbled and her sunglasses slipped from her face. In that instant Dan felt as if lightning had seared his vision. It was impossible. Absolutely impossible, but the woman Joshua Brando held at gunpoint was Shawna Wright.

JESS PARKED the car beneath a cottonwood beside the creek. They'd turned off the road and onto the drive to Pebble Creek Ranch and gone for half a mile before Jess decided to leave the car. He'd found a spot beside the creek where he could hide the car without taking too much time.

The rush of the water over the rocks reminded Celeste of Dan. He was like the water, tumbling over and around any obstacle in his way. She had to believe that at the end of the day, they would both be safe.

"I think if we walk in we'll have the element of surprise," Jess said.

Celeste held out the gun that he'd given back to her.

"You trust me that much?"

"I trust you with Dan's life, so why not mine?" Celeste said.

Jess put a hand on her shoulder. "I never thought there was another woman who could compare with Shawna. But I think Dan found one. And I'm glad for him, Celeste. I'm glad for you both."

They headed up the drive with Familiar at their heels, alert for the sound of anyone around them.

When they could barely see the ranch house through the trees, Jess pulled her off the road and into a copse of trees. "I'm going to leave you here," he said. "And the cat, too."

"What's going on?" Celeste could barely see the house and though there were two cars parked in front, there was no sign of activity.

"I'll check it out. If it's safe, I'll come back for you," Jess said. "Wait here."

He was gone before she could reply, and with her heart beating in her ears, she watched him cover the distance to the house and attach himself to the stone exterior and begin to work his way from window to window.

It was only when she bent to pick up the cat that she realized that Familiar, too, was gone. She looked back toward the house in time to see the cat leap into one of the open windows. She was worried about the cat, but she knew Familiar would protect Dan. Of everyone who might be in the house, she believed the cat was probably the most cunning. At least she hoped so.

She had just gotten comfortable crouched behind a

rock when the still country air was rent with a woman's scream. It was the kind of sound that made the hair on Celeste's neck tingle with electric jolts.

Hugging the rock, she tried to see what was happening but the house looked abandoned. Celeste thought for a moment. She'd promised Jess she would stay where she was. But that had been a female scream. There was another woman in the house, or near it, and she was in trouble.

Hampered by the business suit she'd chosen to wear to Jess's office, Celeste took off the suit jacket and began to slip through the trees. As a child she'd often played games of stealth and speed, and she'd been good at them. She angled toward the house, her gaze flitting from window to window, wondering what had happened to Jess and Familiar.

She made it to within ten yards of the house and realized she'd have to cross the empty yard. There wasn't a shrub or tree to give her even the illusion of cover. Her only chance was that the house wasn't closely guarded.

She gauged the distance again and sprinted across the open yard. The stone exterior of the house felt like heaven as she pressed her body against it and caught her breath. Her heart was hammering and her lungs were painfully tight. It was fear and the rush of adrenaline. But she'd made it. She inched toward the open window Familiar had entered and listened.

There was the murmur of voices coming from another room. Celeste couldn't make out the words, but the anger was obvious. It was Dan's voice raised in anger. And mixed in was a female voice. Her reaction to it was curious—a bone-deep anxiety. Whoever she was, the sound of her voice sent dread through Celeste.

Acting on impulse, Celeste hoisted herself up to the window. She threw one leg over the sill and climbed into what was apparently a music room of some type. A grand piano filled the opposite end of the room, and there were clusters of chairs and sofas, a room where people could relax and enjoy the music if a talented pianist played. Creeping past the piano, Celeste followed the voices, which were growing louder and louder.

The ranch house was large, and she traveled through several rooms before she found herself on the opposite side of the door from the argument. Gently twisting the knob, she cracked the door and peeped into the room.

Her gaze went directly to Dan, who stood with his hands behind his back on the far side. He was staring intently at a woman who slumped in a wing chair. The woman was blond and beautiful and her skin was so pale Celeste wondered if she was ill, or possibly dead. But there was a flutter to her blouse as she breathed.

Celeste felt her own lungs contract painfully as she saw the look on Dan's face as he stared at the woman. He didn't bother to hide his hurt and confusion. Celeste knew instantly that the blonde had been someone he felt strongly about. Someone he might have once loved.

Or perhaps still did.

She held her breath as a strange man rose. He held a gun in his hand and he pointed it at Dan. "You don't have a choice, Mr. Carson. Your mother knew the deal. She may try to pretend she didn't, but she did.'' Celeste had never seen the man's face, but she knew his voice. He was the ''Phantom'' from the ball.

''I don't believe you,'' Dan answered.

''She knew the oil was illegal and she agreed to the terms. She didn't ask any specific questions, and we didn't tell her anything. But she knew. Now you'll buy the oil just as she agreed.''

''Carson Dynamics doesn't have that kind of money.''

Dan was clearly stalling, and Celeste knew if she could determine that, the man could, too.

''I thought you were bringing in a partner,'' the man with the gun said. ''I need to make this sale. Today.'' He clicked the hammer. ''Or the insurance policy on you will give your mother enough funds to honor the deal she made.''

Dan didn't back down. ''I was expecting a partner, but he hasn't arrived.'' He pointed to a small desk in a corner of the room. ''I can call him.''

''In your dreams,'' the man with the gun said.

''You weren't supposed to be here until Sunday,'' Dan reminded him. ''I would have had the deal put together and the money in hand if you'd arrived on time. As it is, you can hardly fault me for not having the money. You're early.''

''I like the advantage of surprise,'' the man said nastily.

''My partner will bring the money,'' Dan said easily. ''But you have to give him time to get here. That's why I wanted to meet here at the ranch, so he could bring cash and we'd feel relatively safe with that much money on hand.''

Celeste could see that Dan's argument was finally winning some points. The man with the gun exchanged a look with the woman. To Celeste's surprise, the woman lifted a finger. It was a gesture that completely escaped Dan's observations, and Celeste reexamined the woman. She was sitting as if she were very sick or drugged. But she was covertly watching everything that happened in the room.

"When will your partner arrive?" the man with the gun asked.

"Soon, Mr. Brando, soon."

"Call me Phil," the man said, ending on a cold chuckle. "You never suspected a thing, did you?"

Dan looked at him. "Never."

"Banking can be such a boring business. But it presents such tremendous opportunities to use other people's money to make your own."

Dan shot him a dirty look. "What have you done to Shawna?"

At the woman's name, Celeste almost gasped. She caught herself and stared once again at the woman slumped in a chair. Was it Shawna Wright? It couldn't be. Dan and Jess both had said she was killed in a car accident.

"She's okay. Her name is Norris now. Shawna Norris. She's quite a powerful woman in the business world in Buenos Aires," the man said. "We've been married for the past nine years and I've put the world at her feet. You could never have given her the things I've provided. You never really understood her. A woman with her brains, her intelligence, her ambition. You would have held her back, stifled her. And I finally made her understand that. In Buenos Aires, we've carved out an empire."

The woman sat up suddenly. "Shut up, Phil. You don't have to spill your guts, you know." In that instant, Celeste saw her eyes and recognized the hot glare of the Mata Hari from the ball.

Celeste was startled by the change in her, but not nearly as startled as Dan. He started toward her, then checked himself, his eyes narrowing. "You're not a prisoner, are you?"

The woman shook her head angrily. "It was a good plan, but Phil couldn't resist gigging you. He's been waiting for years to tell you that he married me and you lost. So, now you know." She reached into her handbag and brought out cigarettes. "Are you happy now, Phil?"

"Not happy. Merely gratified," he said, an edge of anger in his voice. "You think it's fun to deny me my little pleasures. Just remember that I've indulged yours for years."

Dan stood very still, watching both of them. "How did I ever think that I loved you?" he finally said to Shawna. "How was it possible I never saw beneath the surface to who you really are?"

"I'm an incredible actress. I wanted you to love me, so you did. And I was fond of you," she added. "If Phil hadn't come along and made me a better offer, I would have married you."

Celeste had to grip the door to keep from running into the room. Shawna Wright was tearing Dan apart more effectively than if she'd used a knife. She was butchering him, and taking pleasure in doing so. Celeste knew the price Dan would pay for these revelations.

"The day of the wedding—who was in the car?"

"The body?" Shawna laughed out loud. "That was a stroke of luck. It was a young girl who died on the streets. An overdose, if I remember correctly." At

Dan's shocked expression she laughed louder. "We didn't kill her, Dan. She was already dead. Her body was just so damned convenient that we couldn't resist."

"And the limo driver?" Dan's expression was stunned.

"Money can buy almost anything—loyalty, a good story, a convenient wreck." Shawna held out both hands, palms up. "And it fit so perfectly with that damned curse you were always going on about. I'm sorry, I couldn't resist. What better way to start a new life than to die on the way to your wedding." She laughed again.

Celeste could almost feel her hands around the woman's throat. How could anyone be so cruel as to throw another's love back in his face? But thoughts of revenge against Shawna were brought up short when the man who called himself Phil Norris turned and aimed the gun at Dan's head.

"Shawna has had her fun. Now I want my money." He checked his watch. "You've got fifteen minutes to locate your partner and get a line on that money. If I have to kill you, Mrs. Carson will give us the insurance money to cover the deal. She's a smart woman. She'll understand that it's in her best interest."

Celeste made a desperate decision. They had no idea who Dan was expecting as a partner. She looked around the room she was in for something to use as a money satchel. Tiptoeing away from the door, she hurried through the house until she found a bedroom. In the closet she pulled out an empty piece of luggage. It was small, with wheels, perfect for money.

But what to put in it? She started toward a dresser when she felt sharp claws in her leg.

"Meow!"

"It's about time you put in an appearance," Celeste said. "I need something to put in the suitcase and a gun," she added.

Familiar swatted at the case. Wondering what he wanted, Celeste unzipped it. Before she could react, the cat slipped into the case.

"Perfect," she whispered, realizing Familiar's plan was indeed brilliant. When Norris opened the case, Familiar would spring out in his face. It would give Dan, and her, the element of surprise they needed.

"Perfect," she whispered again. "Now for a gun."

"Meow!" Familiar leaped out of the case and headed through the house. He led her unerringly toward a case of weapons. She thanked her lucky stars as she realized someone had already unlocked the case. She didn't know a lot about firearms, but she selected a handgun. Fumbling, she managed to eject the clip. There were nine cartridges in the clip, a full load. She pushed it back into place and tucked the gun into the back of her skirt. It was a precarious assembly, but it would last long enough for her to get in the room. Her hope was to pitch the gun to Dan.

She'd brought the luggage with her, and as Familiar clawed at it, she unzipped the case. "Are you sure?" she asked him as he curled into the darkness of the case.

"Meow," the cat answered, reaching up to bat at the zipper.

Celeste zipped the case, grasped the handle and straightened her back and shoulders. When she walked into that room she had to be tough and ready to cut a deal. And she had to convey to Dan that she had a plan in motion. Success depended on whether Dan had enough trust left in him to believe in her. It was a test of their feelings for one another in the aftermath of Shawna's revelations, and it was the pivot on which their future rested.

She walked to the door, took a deep breath and thrust the door open so that it swung wide and slammed into the wall. She had everyone's attention as she walked into the room.

"I played the devil getting this much money together on short notice. It's a good thing my family has such faith in my business skills." She pulled the case behind her. "And a good thing we believe in hard cash. Here's the money, Dan. Is everything going according to plan?"

Chapter Sixteen

Dan couldn't believe his eyes. How was it possible that Celeste had made it to Pebble Creek Ranch? As far as he knew, she didn't even know the place existed. Yet here she was, looking very determined. What was going on? He felt as if he'd stumbled into a nightmare that blended the worst of his past with all of his future dreams. He looked again toward Shawna to make sure she was real.

The woman staring at Celeste *looked* like Shawna Wright. Same blond hair, blue eyes, perfect figure. Her clothes were designer and clung to her as if they'd been created with her in mind. But there was nothing in her face to remind Dan of the young woman he'd loved so dearly. He started toward Celeste.

"How did you get here?" he asked, knowing that she must have come with someone. Kip? Someone who would help them?

Shawna was on her feet and in Celeste's face in a matter of seconds. "What are you doing here?"

"I'm Dan's partner," Celeste said, not giving a fraction of an inch. "If you want my money you'd better get out of my face." She reached up with her hand and pushed Shawna hard in the chest. The blond stumbled backward before she regained her balance and came back at Celeste.

"You're going to regret that."

"Easy, Shawna," Phil said as he grabbed his wife's shoulders. His expression showed his uneasiness at his wife's open hostility. "If I didn't know you better, I'd say you were jealous," he said accusingly.

"Jealous?" she scoffed. "Of what?"

"Of Dan's relationship with this woman. Miss..."

"Levert," Celeste said clearly. "Celeste Levert."

Shawna said hotly, "She's someone he picked up at a party in Dallas."

"It doesn't matter, as long as she has the money." Phil motioned her to bring the suitcase to him. "We need this money," he said to Shawna. "If we don't get it, we're going to be in big trouble, and we don't want trouble from the petroleum coalition. They don't discuss bad debts," he said, worry furrowing his brow.

"If you want my money, you'd better get her in line," Celeste warned him.

"Open the case," Shawna said, still glaring at Celeste.

Celeste shoved the suitcase toward her. "Be my guest," she said.

Without another word, Shawna grabbed the suitcase and ran the zipper around it. Flipping open the top, she was completely unprepared for the flying black cat. Familiar came out of the case like a demon. He jumped straight onto Shawna's head and dug in. Striking at the cat with her hands, Shawna began to scream and spin around the room, a blur of black cat and whipping blond hair.

Dan saw his moment and dove at Phil, knocking the gun from his hand. They crashed to the floor and struggled for the weapon. Dan was surprised at the strength the man he'd always known as Joshua Brando displayed. For a man in his fifties, Brando— or Norris—was strong.

From the corner of his eye, Dan saw Celeste pull a gun from the back of her skirt. He ducked a punch that Norris threw, and then looked back just in time to see Shawna fling Familiar into the wall. The blow seemed to stun the cat, and Shawna drew back a leg to kick the injured animal.

"Don't make me shoot you," Celeste said. She pulled the trigger and the shot echoed in the room.

Shawna stopped in midkick. The solid oak floor beside her foot showed a hole where the bullet had penetrated.

"I will shoot you," Celeste said, her voice shaking. "You touch one hair on that cat and I'll shoot." She steadied her hand. "Just hope my aim is good and I hit your leg instead of your head."

"You don't have the guts," Shawna said, starting toward Celeste.

Celeste squeezed the trigger again. The shot echoed, and Shawna jumped to the right. A strand of her blond hair drifted down to the floor and settled in the silence that followed.

Shock on her face, Shawna lifted a hand to her hair and found the short ends. "You almost hit me in the face!"

"I told you my aim wasn't great. Don't make me shoot again." Celeste looked at Dan, who was straddling Phil Norris. His fist was drawn back for a punch. She aimed the gun at Phil Norris while keeping an eye on Shawna. "Let him up, Dan. Get against the wall. Both of you." She waved the barrel between Shawna and Phil. "I really don't want to hurt you, but I will. I mean it."

Dan slowly got to his feet. He'd always known Celeste was tough, but he'd never suspected she was so incredible. "Where did you come from?" he asked as he brushed off his clothes. "And by the way, I'm very glad to see you."

"I was in Lomar," she answered. "It's a long story."

Dan's attention was drawn back to the woman he'd almost married.

"My face," Shawna said. "That cat clawed my face. I'm bleeding."

Dan felt nothing for Shawna as he saw that blood streaked her face. He tried to remember what he'd once felt for her. It was hard to believe that the woman standing before him was Shawna. After the car accident, he'd thought he wouldn't be able to live without her. And now?

His mind wanted to believe that there was some terrible mistake at work. He wanted her to have an explanation for the past ten minutes that would somehow set things to right and help him understand the pain he'd suffered for the past ten years. But even as he tried to rationalize her reappearance in his life, his heart rebelled. Mentally, he might be able to try to forgive what she'd done. In his heart, though, he could never forget that she had committed an act of emotional terrorism. There were no excuses for the actions she'd taken.

He reached into his pocket and withdrew a clean handkerchief. Without moving a step closer, he tossed it across to her. "I'm sure you'll heal," he said. He bent to stroke the black cat who watched Shawna through slitted eyes. "You are something special," he said, giving Familiar's chin a good scratch.

"I need a mirror," Shawna said, daubing at the wounds with the handkerchief. "This really hurts," she said, her eyes tearing up.

Dan moved closer to Celeste. He saw that she was staring at Shawna with a mixture of fascination and disbelief. "Are you okay?" he asked Celeste. He started to offer to take the gun but decided that Celeste was holding her own. He couldn't ask for a more able partner.

Celeste nodded. "I'm okay." She addressed her next question to Shawna. "How could you let someone who loved you believe you were dead?"

The blonde continued to blot the trickle of blood that oozed from the scratches Familiar had given her.

"Why would you do such a cruel and unnecessary thing?" Celeste persisted. "Why not say you were breaking the engagement—that you didn't want to marry him? Why torment someone by letting them think you were dead?" With each question, Celeste's voice grew angrier.

Dan put a hand on her shoulder. "It's okay," he said softly, touched by her fury at his pain.

"It's not okay," Celeste answered. "That's one of the cruelest things I've ever heard."

"Meow!" Familiar agreed.

"Oh, don't get on such a high horse," Shawna said curtly. She dropped the handkerchief to the floor.

"When you grow up desperate, you get over those high-flown notions. Before the wedding I got involved in some deals with Phil. It looked as if there might be some difficulty with the law. I needed a new identity. Phil had ingeniously created Joshua Brando, banker. He used that identity to build up business contacts, to learn who might and might not be interested in making money through somewhat questionable means. And when it suited him, he retired Brando from banking and sent him off to live on a ranch on the backside of nowhere. Then he was free to pick up his real identity in Buenos Aires. I needed to dump Shawna Wright and reinvent myself. The wedding was perfect. Every paper in the Southwest carried the tragic story of the young bride killed on her way to the wedding. Shawna was dead, and Shelly emerged."

As she talked, Dan could see her arrogance. He had always known that Shawna was proud of her intelligence, her ability to rethink a business plan and come up with a new angle. He'd been proud of her, too. He had never suspected that beneath that pride was an ego so desperate for attention, so hungry for acknowledgement that she would apply her intelligence in any way that would bring profit, even illegal schemes.

"You deliberately set up a plan that used someone's love for you against them." Celeste's eyes were narrow. "It's a good thing you'll be behind bars for a long time to come."

"Don't count on it," Shawna said, and this time her smile was amused.

Dan walked to the telephone. "The authorities are probably on the way, but I'll just call and make sure," he said. He picked up the portable, punched the buttons, then looked at Celeste. He replaced the receiver. "The lines are dead."

Shawna shrugged one shoulder in a cavalier gesture. "Imagine that."

"They must have been cut," Dan said. "My cell phone is out in the car. I'll go get it and take a look around while I'm out there." He started toward the kitchen. "But first I'm going to get some rope and tie Mr. and Mrs. Norris up," he said. He pushed at the kitchen door but stopped when Celeste called his name.

"I need to talk to you," she said. "There's something you should know."

"I'll be right back." Dan remembered the length of nylon rope he'd left in the utility room. It would be perfect. And it would give him immense pleasure to make sure Joshua Brando-Phil Norris was tied good and tight. "Keep the gun on them and shoot them if they try anything."

"Oh, yes, shoot us," Shawna mocked. "The only trouble is that the phone lines are dead. I'm sure you're right, Dan. Someone cut them. The only question is, was it someone from your side, or maybe some of our men? You haven't considered that possibility, have you?"

Dan didn't like the sensation of a chill at the base of his spine, but he shook his head. "You're really desperate now, Shawna."

"It's Shelly," she corrected him. "Shawna really is dead. My name is Shelly."

"I don't give a damn what name you've assumed," Dan said cooly. "My only concern is that you don't put Celeste in a position where she has to make you bleed from another wound. Or maybe Familiar will just take care of you." He nodded to Celeste. "I'll be right back. If either of them moves, shoot them."

"Dan—"

"I'll be right back." He entered the kitchen and headed for the utility room to the right. The light switch was on the left, and he turned it on. He stopped instantly, drawing in his breath as a tall man stepped out from behind the freezer. It took him a moment to register Rick Hanson's features.

"You almost frightened me to death. It's about time you put in an appearance," he said. He finally saw the gun that Rick held, pointing directly at his heart.

"Stand very still," Rick said slowly.

Dan felt a flicker of concern. "What's wrong? How did you get here?"

Rick stepped forward and without a hint of warning swung the butt of the gun hard into Dan's head. Dan felt himself sliding along the wall, dropping to the floor. He wanted to stop himself but he couldn't. His arms didn't move when he ordered them to do so. His vision began to dim and then there was only blackness.

CELESTE KEPT HER attention on the man and woman who stood against the wall.

"Mind if we sit down?" Shawna asked.

"Stand still," Celeste replied. "Don't move, don't talk. Don't do anything that might make me nervous."

"Make you nervous?" Shawna laughed. "If you got any more nervous you'd develop a permanent twitch." She looked toward the kitchen door. "I wouldn't wait for Dan to come back."

"Shut up," Celeste said. She had a bad feeling about Dan, and she didn't need Shawna reinforcing it.

"Look, you're not really involved in any of this. What would you say if I told you that you could just walk away from here? Just get in one of those cars out there and drive away. All you have to do is press the accelerator and keep going."

"I'd say you're a liar." Celeste didn't want to talk to Shawna, but she found that it was better than listening to her own thoughts. She checked her watch. Dan had been gone three minutes. It seemed like a lifetime.

"He's not coming back."

Celeste felt herself rising to the bait. She disliked the blonde. But she also knew the woman was taunting her, and very effectively. She shifted the gun slightly so that the barrel was aimed more in the direction of the man. "What's *Midnight River*?"

Phil Norris glanced at his wife, then back at Celeste. "It's an oil tanker."

Celeste nodded. It made sense, based on what she'd heard already. Dan had told her nothing, but she'd put together that somehow Carson Dynamics had become involved in buying illegal oil. That oil was obviously coming in on the ship *Midnight River*. Phil Norris and Shawna represented the men who owned the oil. And Dan was supposed to buy it and resell it for a profit. It was the way the oil business operated. Except for one small detail. This oil was coming from a country under embargo.

"Why Dan?" she asked Norris. "Why sell oil to him? There were a thousand other people you could approach."

Norris reached out to his wife and grasped her hand. "Dan was one of the brightest young men I ever met. When I first saw him with Shawna, I envied him. He had everything I had to scrape to put together—intelligence, a bright future, the backing of his family, a natural grace and poise. And Shawna."

Celeste didn't need to hear any more. "You're getting even with him because he was born with more advantages than you." She knew it was true but it was still hard to believe.

"Dan was always so upright. I wondered if he could be tempted by money. I didn't think so, but it was a test. A game, if you will."

"A sick game."

"We knew Dan had the money," Shawna said. "Phil wanted to play games, but it was a matter of expedience. We had a chance at the oil, but we needed someone who could pull the money together fast." She pulled her hand free of her husband's grip.

"But Dan wouldn't bite at the offer." Celeste was guessing now.

"He didn't need the money," Phil said. "We were in something of a pickle," he added. "But Shawna came up with an alternative. It was a simple matter of some real estate manipulation and Dan's mother was in over her head. When she needed to make some money fast, and without Dan discovering it, she didn't ask a lot of questions."

Celeste understood at last. Diana Carson had become involved in this mess as a one-shot deal. "So then you blackmailed her into buying the oil. She did it, hoping Dan would never find out."

Shawna began to pace the floor. "Oh, what a tangled web…"

"Does she know about you?" Celeste asked. She hoped for Dan's sake that his mother did not.

"She never liked me," Shawna said, laughing softly. "Dan couldn't see it. She always thought she was better than me. No, she doesn't know I'm alive. She's talked to me on the phone, but she believes my name is Shelley Norris. Just like my passport says."

"I would never have believed anyone as cruel as you really existed," Celeste said.

The kitchen door swung open and Diana Carson entered. She held a shotgun in her hand and the barrel swung around the room. At the sight of Shawna, she drew in her breath, but the barrel rotated on to Celeste, where it stopped.

"Mrs. Carson," Celeste said, starting toward her. "I—"

"Put down the gun," Diana said. Her voice shook and she glanced again at Shawna.

"Dan may be in terrible danger. He went to get some rope—" Celeste stopped. Something was happening to Diana Carson's face. Strong emotion battled across the carefully made up planes until Diana reached over and took the gun from her hand. "You don't need this," Diana said.

Celeste started to reach for the gun.

"No." Diana stepped back and swung the barrel of the shotgun at Celeste. "I'm sorry," she said. She looked over at the Norrises. "I'm sorrier than I ever thought I'd be."

"Mrs. Carson, what's going on?" Celeste felt her mouth go dry.

"Sit down, Celeste," Diana said, motioning toward the sofa. "Do it now and save us all a lot of grief." She turned to the blonde. "I thought I recognized your voice. There was an inflection there, something so familiar. But I couldn't quite catch it. I guess I didn't want to.''

Shawna walked over to Diana and took the gun from her hand. ''You never thought you'd be in business with your almost daughter-in-law,'' she said. ''Life is amazing.''

Celeste didn't want to believe what she was witnessing. Diana Carson was involved with the crooks. She felt her heart sink. Shawna hadn't been lying. Diana had gotten in over her head. And now Dan would have to face a second serious emotional blow. Betrayed by his ex-fiancée and his mother, all in one day.

Shawna tossed the gun to Phil then took the shotgun from Diana's lifeless hands. ''Get a grip, Diana. We don't have time for hysterics,'' she said.

She pointed the gun at Celeste. ''My husband and I are leaving. I don't think this ranch is healthy for us. And you're going with us.'' She turned to Diana. ''Looks like the cat is out of the bag about your little investment scheme. So, tell Dan that if he wants to see his girlfriend alive again, then he's going to have to come up with the money we need.''

Diana started to protest, then fell silent. Celeste felt a moment of pity for her. She looked suddenly old. Her perfect hair and well-maintained skin seemed to age as Celeste looked at her.

''Take me instead,'' Diana suggested.

''I don't think so,'' Shawna said. She grabbed Celeste's shoulder and pushed her toward the door. ''Let's go.''

''Where?'' Celeste demanded, refusing to be pushed. She caught a glimpse of Familiar under the sofa. She could only hope the cat didn't try anything. Shawna had a gun now, and Celeste didn't doubt that the woman would kill him if he so much as twitched a whisker in her direction.

She didn't want to leave without knowing if Dan was okay. And where had Jess Harper gone? If she could delay, Jess might turn things around. And where was the CIA agent? He'd set up the whole sting. Surely he was keeping an eye on things.

"Don't hold out any hopes for Dan," Shawna said. She went to the kitchen door. "Bring him in here," she called. "I want him to see that we have her."

"Is it really necessary?" Phil said quietly. "The laws we've broken are financial ones. Kidnapping adds another level."

Shawna gave him a look of disgust. "We'll be in South America before anyone begins to look for us. What do we care what we're charged with?"

Diana stood up. "Take me instead, Shawna. Really. I'll go willingly. It won't be kidnapping."

"You always loved your children more than yourself." Shawna looked as if she were considering the idea. "No," she shook her head slowly. "Not this time, Diana."

The kitchen door opened and Dan stumbled through, falling against the sofa. Behind him Rick Hanson held a gun on him. Celeste and Diana started forward to Dan, but Shawna grabbed Celeste and restrained her. "Not so fast. We've got a plane to catch."

"Dan!" Celeste saw him fighting to stay conscious. A trickle of blood oozed down the side of his head from an open gash. She looked at the CIA agent. "I never should have trusted you," she said.

"That's an understatement." Shawna laughed. "Dan, you know CIA agent Rick Hanson. But did you know that he does a little freelance work?" She laughed. "With Rick on our side there was no way for Carson Dynamics to wiggle free." She went to Dan and nudged his shoulder with the gun barrel until he looked up at her. "I'll call you in two hours and tell you where to deliver the money. If you don't, Celeste will die and you and your mother will be charged with importing illegal oil. It's a no-win situation, Dan. Accept it and do what I tell you. Or you'll truly have a dead girlfriend on your hands."

Chapter Seventeen

Dan felt as if one of the ranch horses had kicked him in the head with great gusto, but he forced himself to focus on what was happening. Celeste's safety was his primary concern, and he saw that so far she was unharmed.

He was still confused about the ever changing loyalties of the players. Rick Hanson's betrayal had been a surprise, but one Dan knew he should have anticipated with more accuracy. He'd never trusted the CIA agent. He cursed his foolishness in not examining Hanson's credentials more closely. He'd been so concerned with protecting his mother that he'd failed to delve deeply enough into Hanson's sting proposal.

Diana's appearance in the room had him confused. He remembered that he'd sent her to the barn, but she'd come back into the house and she looked as if she might be ill. His gaze shifted to Shawna as she grasped Celeste's shoulder. Dan was struck by a wave of anger compounded by the helplessness of his position.

His fury grew at the idea that Shawna intended to take Celeste as a hostage. "Leave Celeste and you'll get your money," he said slowly, working hard to enunciate. His head was clearing, but he was still dizzy and his tongue felt thick.

"I'm sure you're *dying* to cooperate with us," Shawna drawled sarcastically. She looked at Phil Norris. "Let's get out of here. There's no telling who else might show up."

"What about the guy in the barn?" Rick asked.

Dan knew they were referring to Kenneth Martin, and he felt another hope slip away. Kenneth had been badly injured by the beating, but Dan had counted him as a possible rescue. Now, though, he was afraid Celeste's cousin was about to die.

"Is he conscious?" Shawna asked. "If he gets in the way, kill him. Remember, he's a loose end for you, unless you plan on retiring from the CIA and moving to South America with us."

"Not yet," Rick said, smiling. "But that bonus you promised me will go a long way toward the retirement I need."

"Finish this up and you'll get your money," Shawna assured him. "Repair the phone lines. I want to be sure Dan can get the location where he should wire our money."

"It's the weekend," Dan stated thickly. "Banks won't be open."

"You have enough clout to find a banker," Shawna said, laughing. "We have to go. It was good to see you, Dan. And you, Mrs. Carson. Good doing business with both of you."

Dan's gaze locked with Celeste's. She was standing tall, and she nodded at him to let him know she wasn't afraid. At Shawna's urging, she turned to walk out on the porch. At the doorway she paused and turned back. "Remember, Dan, old friends are the best."

"Like me," Shawna said brightly, prodding Celeste out the door.

"I love you, Dan," Celeste called back. "From the moment I saw you at the Sweetheart Ball talking with your *friends*. I knew I loved you."

Dan's full attention was on Celeste's words. She was telling him something, he just didn't know what. He started forward, ignoring the throb of pain in his head and the following nausea.

The black shadow that snaked in between Shawna's and Celeste's legs was not as tall as their knees, and Dan almost called out to the cat. Then he knew that Familiar was his last chance. Celeste was slipping out of his grasp, and it would be up to the cat to save her. If anyone could.

"Don't even think about it," Rick Hanson said as he moved close enough so that the barrel of his gun pressed into Dan's temple and he pushed Dan back into a sitting position.

"Stop it," Diana Carson said. She went to Dan and examined the wound on his head. "He needs a doctor."

"He can have one as soon as he transfers the funds." Rick was in no hurry to provide medical attention.

"You people lied to me every step of the way," Diana said, her voice brittle with anger. "It was all a trap."

"And you walked into it," Rick agreed. "Now it's time to pay up. Just remember, get the money to Mrs. Norris and no one will get hurt."

"And what about you?" Dan asked. He could still

hear Celeste outside. They had put her into the back seat of one of the cars but they were having difficulty starting the motor. It was only a brief delay, but it was Dan's only chance. Once they drove away, he might not be able to do anything to save her. He had to sway Rick, if he could. "Do you really think they'll give you your share? This is a woman who left me thinking that she'd died in a tragic accident."

"Incredible," Rick agreed. "What a mind."

"Why should she pay you?" Dan asked him. With each passing minute, he felt stronger, more clear-headed. But would he be able to take Rick in a fight? He wouldn't know until he tried.

"That's right," Diana said, getting up to pace the room. "If they don't give you your share, what can you do? Report it to the cops?"

"Sit down," Rick told her. "I won't report it and neither will you. You're in this up to your ears. That's the beauty of the plan."

"Don't be foolish," Diana responded, increasing her pacing. "You're right, I'm in this as deep as you are. But I'm not counting on those two to give me my money." She continued to walk, angling behind the sofa where Dan sat. Her steps were rapid, moving to and fro across the room. "I'd be careful, Hanson," she added. "Once the Norrises have the money, why should they pay you?" She let her point hang in the room.

Dan saw that the CIA agent was considering what she'd said. It made a lot of sense and he reinforced the issue. "Think about it. You were stupid not to get your share up front. If something happens to any of us, who's going to take the fall? They'll be out of the country. You'll be the one with the dead bodies on your hands.''

Car doors slammed. There was obviously something wrong with the car, but he couldn't catch a clear view through the lacy sheers at the window. Celeste's dark hair was visible in the back seat of the car, and Phil walked around the car to the front and lifted the hood. Shawna's voice was raised in frustration. Dan could only hope that his luck held out and the car continued to give them trouble—and that Familiar was with Celeste.

"Just let us go and we'll leave your part out of this," Diana said smoothly.

"Keep it up and I'll be forced to shoot you," Rick answered with equal ease.

"What would you do with so many dead people?" Diana asked.

"Easy enough to say you attacked me," Rick said.

"Even me, a woman? You think they'll believe you had to shoot a woman?" Diana asked. She stumbled in her pacing and almost fell. "Damn shoe," she said, bending down to rub her ankle. "Dan," she said, on a small cry of pain. "I think I've twisted my ankle. Can you help me?"

Dan eased to his feet. For a second he was dizzy, then he gained his balance and went to help his mother. His feelings toward her were mixed. He was angry with her for getting involved in such a scheme, but Diana hadn't known the oil was illegal, at first. "Let me see it," he said, bending down. As he did, he caught sight of the gun that had been knocked out of Phil Norris's hand during the struggle.

"Ouch!" she cried out, though he hadn't touched her. "Don't be so rough." Their actions were hidden by the sofa, and Diana was putting on a good front as Dan recovered the gun, slipping it into his pocket.

"You need an ice pack," he said, helping her hobble to a chair.

"Don't think you're going to the kitchen," Rick said. "What are you two up to?"

"You get the ice," Dan suggested.

Rick moved toward the kitchen door, as if to block their escape. "I don't think so. Sit down, Carson. I've had enough of you. Both of you sit down and shut up."

Dan was just ready to bring up the gun he'd recovered when the kitchen door swung in with such force that Rick was smashed in the side and knocked off balance. He stumbled across the room directly toward Dan, who obliged by chopping the butt of his gun down squarely on the CIA agent's head. Rick fell to the floor in an unconscious heap.

Dan spun, dropped behind the sofa and lifted the gun.

"Don't shoot," Jess Harper said as he slipped into the room.

"Jess!" Dan said. "How did you get here?"

"I came with Celeste," he said, motioning behind him. Kenneth appeared in the kitchen. He was badly bruised, but there was a dark glint in his eyes. "And we have reinforcements," he said, stepping aside.

Trell Sylvest entered the room. Dan lifted his gun, but Jess waved a hand at him. "He hid in the baggage well on my plane, then tailed us in a rental car. He's come to help."

"Celeste is in danger," Trell said. "If we're going to save her, we must work together."

Dan scrutinized Trell's expression. He wasn't certain he could trust him.

Trell lifted his hand revealing the wires that dangled from his fingers. "I removed the distributor caps from the cars," he said with a tight smile. "They won't be leaving, but we must act together to prevent them from harming Celeste."

Dan lowered the gun. It had been a day of surprises, and Trell was just another in a long list. "Okay," he agreed. "Phil and Shawna are both armed," he said as he glanced out the window. "And they're headed back in here."

As he spoke there was the sound of footsteps on the porch.

Trell moved quickly to shift behind the front door as Jess and Kenneth slipped into the kitchen. They would attempt a flanking maneuver outside, hoping to work their way to Celeste if she remained in the car. Dan grasped Rick's leg and dragged him behind the sofa. He sprang over it and took a seat. "Let them get inside," he said to Trell. "Be sure Celeste is clear."

"I'll grab Celeste," Trell reassured him. "You take care of the man."

Dan had a split second of concern, but there wasn't time for him to doubt Trell. He held the gun beside his leg as he struck a casual pose.

The door opened and Shawna entered, her gun drawn as her gaze swept the room. Diana and Dan sat innocently on the sofa.

"Where's Rick?" she asked.

"In the kitchen," Dan responded. "Something wrong with the car?" he asked innocently. Trell was concealed by the door only inches from Shawna. Dan was certain she would sense his presence, would turn to discover him, and that Celeste would be killed as she stood in the yard.

He glanced out the window and saw her standing beside the car, looking into the house, though she couldn't see him. Her dark eyes were bright with worry. She'd tried to warn him that Jess was there—that there was yet hope. But even though she was only twenty yards away, she might has well have been across an ocean.

"You're looking a little lovesick," Shawna said cruelly. She saw something in Dan's face and turned to look out the window. "She's fine, as long as you get the money to us. You know, Dan, emotional involvement can be a real problem for a businessman. Especially one cursed in love." Her mouth curled up in a hard smile.

"My problem isn't the fact that I care about people, Shawna. My mistake was in the person I chose to love." He had to keep her attention. He saw Trell shifting positions, hoping for a better angle at which to jump her. But it wasn't the right move. Trell might get Shawna, but Phil could still kill Celeste. Through the gauze of the curtains he saw Celeste brush her long, dark hair back from her face and turn to look into the woods.

"Your problem is that everything has always been handed to you and you just assumed that the rest of your life was going to be easy," Shawna said with some heat.

Dan knew that Shawna was watching him closely, and he had to keep her attention. "I pity you, Shawna. You grew up with nothing and you've arranged your life so that's what you'll end up with."

"Save your pity," she said hotly.

Dan was delighted to see that his words angered her. Pride was her weakness, and he meant to goad her as much as possible. "Even if you do get away with the money, that's all you'll have. You don't love Phil. You don't love anyone. Especially not yourself. Because you're basically unlovable. You had everything. You were loved, even better than loved, you were worshipped, and you threw it away. I guess it's true when they say a person can't escape their roots. You were a desperate child, hungry for material things and pathetically unloved. Now you're just older and more desperate. More pathetic."

"Shut up." Shawna started toward him and Dan felt the thrill of elation. She was falling into the trap.

"You walked out on a life that anyone would envy. I would have given you anything you wanted. Given, Shawna. It would have been yours for the asking."

"Nobody gives anything," Shawna said. She swung the gun curtly in his direction. "People get what they take. That's the way life works. You didn't have anything to give me except your love. Sure, you had big dreams and lots of promises, but you can't eat promises and you can't spend dreams."

"I told you it would take work, and it did. But my business is thriving. And it's legitimate. I could have given you anything you desired, if you'd given me a little time." For the first time he saw a chink in her hard wall of emotions. Her gaze shifted to Diana.

"She always thought she was better than me. I sensed it from the first minute we met. She knew I grew up poor. I was never good enough for her son. I never would have been. It was pointless to think she would accept me as a daughter."

"That's not true, Shawna," Diana said softly. "Dan loved you so much that I couldn't help but love you. Whatever negative things you felt from me were imagined. I had only one concern about you and Dan, and that was the Arleotta curse known to my family as the Carson curse."

Behind the door, Trell seemed to stiffen, then relaxed before Shawna noticed him. "The curse." Shawna nodded. "I'm not stupid. That's something you made up to keep Dan and me apart."

She took a step toward the kitchen and Dan saw Trell's opportunity slide further away. She was moving away from him instead of toward him.

Diana shook her head. "I only wish it were true. Long ago, Maria Arleotta put that curse on me because I married the man she loved. She wanted Jake to love her. When he didn't, she cursed us both. The curse was, and is, very real."

"Shawna! Hurry it up!" Phil called from outside.

"Right." The hint of softness in Shawna's eyes disappeared. They turned icy blue. "Now tell me what you did to the car," she said. "I didn't come in here to dissect the past. Phil and I have plans."

"I don't know about the car."

"Give me the key to yours," she said, holding out her free hand and bringing the gun to Dan's chest. "Now."

Dan reached into his pocket, knowing that Trell had taken the distributor caps from both vehicles. "Sure," he said.

"Slow and easy," she warned.

"Give up now, Shawna, and I'll do what I can to make it easier for you," Dan said as he extracted the keys. He held them aloft. "Leave Celeste and I'll get you the money. You can have the oil and do whatever you can with it. Just leave Celeste and drop Carson Dynamics from the deal.''

Her laughter rang out as she walked across the room and grasped the keys. ''You still don't realize that I'm smarter than you. You might be able to convince little innocent Celeste of something like this, but I've been around the block. Remember, Dan, never try to con a con.'' She snatched the keys. ''Get that money wired to us if you want to see her again.''

Outside the window, Dan caught sight of Jess's curly head, followed by Kenneth's dark one. They were in position. And so was Shawna. He nodded once. It was the signal Trell had been waiting for. Shawna was away from the door and her attention was distracted by the keys. As Trell dove at her back, Dan rolled off the sofa and pulled his mother beneath him as they tumbled across the floor. Trell and Shawna fell forward to their knees.

There was an explosion as Shawna pulled the trigger on the gun and the pillow on the sofa where Dan had been sitting exploded into a cloud of feathers.

Dan covered his mother until he was certain the gunfire had stopped, and then he continued in a hard roll toward the door. He hit the porch running and was halfway across the boards when he saw a black bolt of lightning launch itself at Phil Norris.

Phil brought the gun up and squeezed off a shot. Familiar gave a wail of pain and fury, but his attack was undaunted. He landed on Phil's chest and dug in with all four sets of claws.

Dan closed the distance to Celeste, clutching her in his arms as he dragged her to safety behind the car.

"Stay low," he ordered as he started to Familiar's rescue.

As he darted around the car, he saw Jess. The look on his friend's face was deadly, and Dan watched as Jess smashed his fist into Phil's ear. The crook stumbled into Kenneth, who neatly pinned him. Dan lifted Familiar into his arms as Jess stepped forward and delivered the knockout punch.

Phil Norris, alias Joshua Brando, dropped to the dirt like a sack of potatoes. Jess kicked the gun away from Phil's hand.

Dan held the cat in his arms and felt the sticky flow of blood. Because of the thick black fur, he couldn't tell how badly Familiar was injured.

"Celeste," he called. "Help me."

She was beside him in a second, her hands moving expertly over the cat. "It's his shoulder," she said. "Let's get him inside."

Familiar's eyes were closed and Dan felt a second of despair. The brave cat had continued his attack even when he was badly wounded.

"I'll tie this one up," Jess offered. "There's some rope in the barn."

Dan ran up the steps with Celeste at his side.

When they entered the ranch, Diana and Trell were tying Shawna in a chair. Rick Hanson's hands were already bound behind his back, and he was moaning back to consciousness on the floor.

"You haven't won yet," Shawna said.

"If she says anything else," Dan told Diana, "gag her. And make it a tight gag. I've heard enough." He settled onto the sofa with Familiar in his lap and Celeste at his side.

"I hope that black devil is dead," Shawna said.

Dan ignored her, turning Familiar in his hands so that he could find the gash that ran long the cat's left shoulder. Familiar's eyes were closed but his breathing was regular.

"It looks like the bullet grazed him," Celeste said as her fingers gently probed the wound.

"Me-ee-ee-ow," Familiar cried weakly.

"It's par for the course with the Carson family," Shawna taunted. "A black cat and a family curse. What was it you called it, Diana, the Arleotta Curse? Perfect."

Beside Dan, Celeste went rigid. Dan turned to her. "What?"

Celeste stroked Familiar's head, but her hands had begun to tremble. "What did you call the curse?" she looked at Shawna.

"Ask Diana. She's the superstitious one," Shawna answered.

Celeste ignored Shawna and turned to Dan's mother. "The name, was it Arleotta?"

"Yes," Diana said, moving closer to Celeste. "What is it? You're white as a ghost."

"Arleotta is my mother's maiden name."

For a moment there wasn't a sound in the room. Dan felt the cat shift in his lap and he saw that Familiar had opened his eyes and was watching Celeste.

"Maria Arleotta," Celeste almost whispered.

"My god," Diana said, leaning on the sofa for support. "That's her." Diana was as pale as Celeste. "That's the woman who cursed my family."

Celeste closed her eyes briefly. "Now it all makes sense," she said. "Now I understand why my mother felt so strongly about the marriage my father arranged." She shook her head and turned to where

Trell was watching her from across the room. She turned back to Dan. "My mother was in love with your father. When he didn't marry her, she cursed him and his descendants. It was a terrible thing she did."

Dan saw the shame in Celeste's eyes. "We'll figure this out," he promised her. "If your mother put it on, then she can take it off."

Celeste shook her head. "You don't understand. There's no such thing as a Gypsy curse." She looked at Diana. "You know that. Deep in your heart. It was just easier to go on all this time pretending that someone had brought unhappiness down on your family." She focused on Dan. "You've suffered terrible things, and you believed it was because of my mother." She rose unsteadily to her feet. "Trell, will you take me back to Lomar? Will you take me home?"

Trell stepped forward. "Of course, Celeste. Anything you want."

Dan reached out and caught Celeste's hand. "Wait, Celeste. We can work this out."

She shook her head. "My parents were right. How long would it be before something went wrong? An argument or a bad business deal. How long before you wondered if I'd put a curse on you?" She wiped the tears from her cheeks. "No matter what I want for myself, there's too much past, too much history. I can't escape it, Dan. And you can't avoid yours." Tears shimmered in her eyes but her voice was strong. "We're different. Hoping and dreaming won't change that. At last I understand. And I've short-changed my parents and Trell in all of this. If I was so wrong about everything else, perhaps I've been wrong about him, too. I have a lot of amends to make." She bent down and patted Familiar's head.

Familiar's paw hooked out and snagged her hand, holding her in place.

Dan caught her hand, too, and held it. "Don't do this," he said. "Give it some time. We need to talk."

Diana stepped forward, touching Celeste's shoulder. "The past is over and done, Celeste. Don't throw away the future because of my foolishness and your mother's pain."

Dan tightened his grip on Celeste's hand. He felt as if he were trapped in a hall of mirrors. No matter where he turned, he saw loss. "You say the curse isn't real. But if I lose you, it proves that it's real. It doesn't matter if you walk out because you don't love me or because you think you're doing the right thing. The end result is heartbreak. Think, Celeste. Think of the future. Think what we have together, what we can build."

Celeste scooped Familiar into her arms. "For the first time in a long while, I see my future clearly. I know what I need to do. First I'm taking Familiar to the vet, and then I'm going home to my family, to my people. And I'll assume the duties I was born to carry out. I—" She couldn't finish as tears began to fall down her cheeks. "I have to do this, Dan. Honor my wishes and don't attempt to change my mind."

Dan slowly released his grip. He had thought he could never experience a pain worse than what he'd felt when he was told Shawna was dead. Now he knew that pain came in all degrees and colors. Letting Celeste go was not heartbreak; it was anguish. But in the brief time they'd had together, he knew that it was the only thing that he could do. All her life someone had tried to manage her, to bend her to their design and plan. The freedom to make her own deci-

sions was the thing she'd fought hardest to attain.
Even if she chose to walk away from him and break
his heart.

With the cat in her arms Celeste turned and walked
out the front door. Trell followed behind her, softly
closing the door.

Chapter Eighteen

Ouch! Dr. Dolittle never hurt me like that when he was doctoring a wound. This veterinarian probably tends cows instead of the more delicate felines. Ouch! But he's pronouncing me healthy to travel. Maybe I should have faked being sicker and tried to get Celeste to stay at the ranch. The truth is, I don't know what to do. It's a rare moment in the life of a supersleuth when I see the mystery solved and then the romantic leads walk off in separate directions. Never, in all of my wildest dreams, did I consider that Celeste would return to Lomar and marry Trell.

He's not a bad guy, mind you. A little overbearing and not above moving into Celeste's family like a son, but he did show up when the chips were down. He cares about Celeste, though he doesn't know how to show it. But he isn't right for the Golden Goddess. Celeste is Dan's. That's plain for anyone to see.

So, what am I going to do? Celeste has already called her mother and told her to prepare for the wedding. She's going to marry this man before she gets cold feet and backs out. But this is a mistake—a tragic mistake. And if anyone is going to stop it, I suppose it's me.

The question here is how. Perhaps some time during the ceremony I'll see my chance. After listening to the plans Celeste was making on the phone, I think I'll enjoy the food. And dancing! But the ceremony can't conclude with an actual wedding, unless Dan steps in. And I'll make certain he appears.

CELESTE WATCHED the Texas landscape pass by the car window. It was a long drive to Lomar, and one that she found awkward with Trell. She kept looking over at him. She'd underestimated him. As a man and as an ally.

"I'm sorry, Trell. I judged you without giving you a chance."

He nodded. "It's partly my fault. I never knew how to approach you. Long ago, back in school, I wanted to ask you out, but I was afraid. You were so serious, so beautiful. When I realized I had fallen in love with you, I took up the matter of marriage with your father in the traditional way. I should have spoken with you, given you a chance to get to know me. Things are changing, even for us."

She heard the wistful tone in his voice and couldn't help a smile. "Things are changing. The women in my generation are balking at being so completely controlled."

"Our entire way of life will change. We've given up our roving life and settled into a community, and now the changes will be gradual. It's the natural process, so I'm not complaining. It's just difficult to accept." He turned to her and smiled. "It makes me feel old and a little uncertain."

Celeste understood. She'd thought she was a new type of woman for her family—independent and strong, capable of making her own way in the business world. But she'd been wrong. She was, after all, her mother's daughter. Her rebellion had moved her community forward toward a new time and place, but she hadn't broken free of the past.

The old stereotypes of the Roma prevailed—horse traders, fortune-tellers, a people who loved music and dance, and who could put a curse on an enemy.

She couldn't be angry with her mother for playing on a romantic rival's weakness—Diana's own willingness to believe in curses. Curses were not real, and Maria knew that better than anyone.

"Are you sure you want to do this, Celeste?" Trell asked. "I've given this a lot of thought, and it isn't right that you should be forced to marry me."

"No one is forcing me. This is the way it has to be. Maybe the next generation, my own daughters, will have the choice of freedom."

"You spoke with your mother about the ceremony?" Trell's voice held a note of eagerness.

"It'll be Tuesday," Celeste said, and she refused to allow the hard lump of emotion to lodge in her throat. In a few short days she would become Trell's bride. The Roma did not take the vows of marriage lightly. She knew that once she accepted Trell as her husband, she would put her entire abilities into making the union work. Divorce wasn't an option for the leader of the Gypsies.

"I'll make you a good husband," Trell said. "I want the position of honor, but I also see that you're a woman that any man would be lucky to have as a wife. Perhaps we can start our own business, something where you could apply the skills you've learned."

Celeste realized that Trell was being as generous as he knew how. He recognized her need to work, to prove herself in the marketplace. His gesture was not wasted on her, even though it finally brought the lump into her throat and the tears to her eyes. "Thank you, Trell. I also underestimated your kindness. I see that we've got many things to learn about each other."

"In time," Trell said. "In time."

DAN SAT AT HIS desk and watched the flow of his employees. They were all busy, all smiling. Several of them had brought the morning newspaper where there was a lengthy story about the arrest of Buenos Aires jet-setters Mr. and Mrs. Phil Norris, alias Joshua Brando and Shawna Wright and a crooked CIA agent.

No one in the office, except Diana, connected Dan and Carson Dynamics to the story. The CIA had been so grateful to Dan, Jess and Diana for nailing Rick and capturing the Norrises that they had not laid charges against Diana for her involvement. She'd come away from the scandal with a stern warning to be more careful of who she did business with. Diana had sworn a solemn vow to leave the oil trading up to Dan.

Except for Celeste's incredible decision to go back to Lomar, everything had turned out perfectly.

Dan took a breath at the sharp pain that any thought of Celeste brought to him. Her decision had been so cold, so damn selfish. Maybe it was just that whenever he fell in love, it would always be with a woman who couldn't love him back. Maybe there *was* something wrong with him. Maybe he was cursed.

He scratched his chest, finally slipping a finger inside the buttons. He'd never had a place that itched like the tiny wound he'd received in the maze. It should have healed days ago, but instead it continued to annoy him. Maybe there'd been some type of bacteria on the Cupid's arrow. He called his secretary and asked Betty to make a doctor's appointment. Enough was enough.

He looked up in surprise when the door to his office opened and his mother stepped into the room. "Kip is waiting at the airport. Let's go."

"Where?" he asked. He was still annoyed with his mother. She'd been pushing him hard about Celeste, urging him to take action before it was too late. Well, that showed what she knew. Celeste had walked out on him. She'd made her decision and Dan was not about to go and beg.

"Don't ask questions. I just got a call from a cat, and if I'm willing to believe he told me to get you to Lomar, then the least you can do is go."

Dan shook his head. "Not on your life."

"Dan, it was Familiar. He sounded frantic, as if something were wrong. I tried to call Celeste's family, but there's no answer. I'm concerned that something has happened to her."

Rising to his feet, Dan studied his mother. He couldn't tell if he was being played for a fool or if she was seriously concerned. "If this is some kind of trick..." He let the threat hang.

"After Shawna and Celeste, I wouldn't dare to meddle in your affairs." Diana sighed. "But we have to make sure Celeste is all right. Let's go."

For Dan, the trip seemed both an eternity and a mere second. While Kip piloted the jet in and out of the clouds, Dan vacillated between worry over Celeste and fear that his mother had tricked him.

They were at the airport in Lomar in just over an hour, and Dan felt his anxiety rise as he saw that Kip was coming with them. Concern for Celeste skyrocketed. "Let's go," he said brusquely.

It was late afternoon, and though it was mid-February, the day had a springlike quality about it.

"I'm sure you haven't thought of it," Diana said as the car pulled into a local florist shop, "but I took the liberty of ordering a bouquet for Celeste's mother, on the chance she's still in the hospital."

When Kip went in to get the flowers, Dan confronted his mother. "Is Celeste in danger or not?"

"Mortal danger," Diana said. "I know you, Dan. You wouldn't be here if you didn't want to. Accept that you love her and do whatever it takes to win her. For once, take the advice of your mother. We're here, and we shouldn't leave unless Celeste comes with us."

Dan turned to look out the window. His mother was right. He'd come to Lomar not because he really believed Celeste was in jeopardy, but because he wanted to see her. When Kip handed the flowers into the back seat, he smiled at the huge box of red roses.

"Three dozen?" he asked.

"Seven. For good luck. Go, Kip. Familiar really did call, Dan. Something's going on here, and I have this definite feeling that if we don't hurry we'll be too late."

Lomar was a small town, and with a few directions, they found the Levert home. Dan and his mother got out in front of the house while Kip drove on to find a parking space. The entire street was crowded with cars, and Dan felt his stomach tighten. The Leverts were having a party.

The sound of music came from the backyard. As Dan drew closer, he felt as if the music had a life of its own. It was wild, exotic music that spoke of happiness and loss, of passion and pleasure and suffering. He caught his mother's arm and drew her around the house to the backyard where he stopped.

There were over a hundred people on the lawn, and they were all watching a beautiful dark-haired woman dance around a blazing fire. It was early dusk, and Dan was transfixed by the leaping tongues of fire and the swirling red-and-black skirts of the dancer against the beauty of the sky. When the male dancer appeared in the circle, he knew it was Trell. The woman who danced with a sensuous strength was Celeste.

"It's the wedding," Dan said. He stood as if rooted to the spot.

"Let's go," Diana said, grabbing his elbow and stepping toward the dancers.

But Dan wouldn't budge. "It's too late. She's made her choice, and she should be allowed to live her own life. That's all she ever really wanted, and I respect her enough to give her that freedom."

"Hogwash!" Diana snapped. "I never took you for a fool or coward. Get in there and dance!" Diana pushed Dan forward.

When he balked again a small black shadow darted across the lawn. Familiar leaped through the air and landed squarely on Dan's butt. Clawing and biting, Familiar drove Dan forward and into the circle of dancers.

The fiddle players faltered as half the guests rose to their feet. Dan looked around and saw the shock on the faces of everyone present. Except Celeste. There was no shock on her face—only disbelieving happiness. It was the only thing Dan needed to see. He didn't know the dance or the custom, but he knew the woman, and he knew his own heart.

He caught Celeste's extended hand and matched his movements to hers as they stepped in a circle before the fire. Trell made a low bow to Dan and stepped away from the dancers. Dan knew that he had conceded with as much grace as any man could muster, and he knew that Celeste had been wrong about one thing. Trell would make a good leader for her people.

From out of the darkness, Ramone Levert stepped into the path of the dancers. Dan maneuvered Celeste so that he could protect her. But before he could lift a hand, Trell went to Ramone and put a hand on his shoulder.

"Just because she's your daughter doesn't mean she should be denied happiness," Trell said softly. "Let her go, Ramone."

Dan matched gazes with Trell, nodding once. With that action, Trell had demonstrated a leadership that would serve Celeste's people well in the future. Ramone Levert stepped back, clearing the way for the dance to continue.

And then Dan had no thoughts for anything except the woman before him. The fire leaped and danced in Celeste's dark eyes, and he seemed unable to look anywhere else as they gave themselves to the music and danced the Gypsy wedding dance.

CELESTE SAT in the straight-backed chair, the hem of her brightly colored skirt pulled just over her knees as the bread was placed on her left knee and the salt on the right. She looked up to laugh at Dan's amazed expression as he followed the instructions offered by the men of the community. It was a traditional Gypsy marriage, and Dan was doing the best he could with a custom that he found baffling.

As Dan came to sit in front of her, Celeste leaned forward. "Salt and bread are the symbols of life. Take a piece of bread and put some of the salt on it," she instructed. She felt the eyes of everyone in her community watching.

Dan did as she instructed, never letting his gaze leave her. There was complete trust in what he did, and Celeste felt as if her heart might break. "When you eat the bread, we'll be married," she said.

"It can't possibly be this simple," Dan answered.

"It's this simple and this hard. We'll be married before my people in a ceremony as binding as any legal document. You'll be my husband."

Dan took a portion of bread and salted it and put it in his mouth. He swallowed. "I love you," he said.

Celeste picked up a small piece of bread, salted it and ate it. "The salt and bread are tokens of life and harmony," she whispered so that only he could hear.

Her father stepped forward placing a hand on both of their heads. "I bless this union of my headstrong daughter and the man who refused to give up on her. I want lots of strong and healthy grandchildren," he said, stepping back.

Celeste's mother stepped forward. "There is a time when love and passion can tumble the boundaries of tradition. This is such a time. We welcome Dan into our family."

Celeste rose and Dan followed suit so that they stood before the people. Diana was in the front row, her face alive with happiness. Beside her, Familiar stood watching.

"Kiss me," Celeste whispered.

"Now that's a request I've been waiting to hear." Dan gathered her into his arms and kissed her.

Celeste knew the passion of the kiss contained all the hope and despair that had raged within Dan for the past two days. She responded with an equal measure of emotion. In the distance there was the sound of clapping and laughter, and she slowly came to realize that the commotion was directed at her and Dan. They ended the kiss, both slightly stunned.

Ramone nodded, then turned to address the gathered witnesses. "Because Celeste has chosen to marry outside our people, and because she is my only heir, it is time to select a new leader." He held out his hand and Celeste pulled up the chain. Without a bit of hesitation she looped it over her head and stepped forward, Dan's hand still in hers. She turned to Trell. "I give this to the man my father has chosen as his heir. I could not give my place to a better leader. I know he'll guide our community with wisdom and generosity in the years to come." She placed the ring in his hand and stepped back.

While the crowd's attention was on Trell, Celeste took Dan's hand and pulled him into the gathering shadows. "Let's leave," she said.

"Can we?" Dan looked around.

"After we settle one thing." Celeste patted his chest. "Wait here." She slipped away and in a moment returned with both their mothers. "Mother, I want you to tell Diana that there is no such thing as a Gypsy curse," she said.

Maria Levert nodded. She turned to Diana. "Long

ago I was jealous of you. I didn't know you, and I really didn't know Jake. I fell in love with who I thought he was. And I did a terrible thing. I used my heritage as a weapon, not because I had the power to cast a spell or a curse, but because I had the ability to make you afraid. The only weapon I had was your fear, and I'm sorry for using it.''

Diana took Maria's hand. "I was a fool. I'm not superstitious, but it was easy to blame things that went wrong on a curse rather than take responsibility for my own actions. You did no harm that I didn't compound. Your apology is accepted, and I welcome you as a part of my family.''

Celeste kissed her mother's cheek, and then Diana's. "I love you both,'' she told them. "And now Dan and I are leaving.''

"A honeymoon?'' Diana asked.

"I want to apply for a formal license and make this wedding as legal as the state of Texas can make it,'' Dan replied. "I'm thinking if we do it twice, maybe it'll put the odds in our favor.''

Maria looked from one to the other. "I think your love is all the luck you'll ever need.''

"We need to get Familiar,'' Celeste said. "Where is he?''

"He was eating an entire pork loin, and then I saw him headed into the house,'' Maria answered.

"I'll get him,'' Celeste said.

"I'll go with you.'' Dan gathered her hand to his chest. "I'm not letting you out of my sight.''

They entered the house and found Familiar sitting on the kitchen counter. The telephone was off the hook and someone was calling the cat's name.

"What in the world…?" Celeste wondered as she picked up the phone. "Hello."

"This is Ashley Brunston," a female voice said. "I'm looking for a black cat named Familiar. I got a call from this number…"

Celeste felt her heart sink. "Are you his owner?" she asked.

"He belongs to my sister-in-law, Eleanor," Ashley explained. "But he's a cat who likes to travel. Was that him who called?"

Celeste held the phone to her chest. "It's Familiar's family," she said, reaching out to stroke the cat's head. She spoke into the phone. "Yes, he's here and he's safe. I have to tell you he's the most remarkable animal I've ever known. I'd love to keep him."

"Eleanor and Peter have been wild with worry, and so have my husband and I. Where is he? We're close to San Antonio."

Celeste spoke to Dan. "They're in San Antonio. Can we take Familiar to them?" she asked.

"Sounds like the perfect beginning of our honeymoon."

Celeste reached out and touched Dan's cheek. "When I think I can't love you more, I find I can." She spoke into the phone. "We'll bring him to you. We have quite a story to tell you and Familiar plays a big role."

"We'll be waiting," Ashley answered.

Celeste wrote the directions, then said goodbye and replaced the phone. She gave Familiar another scratch and turned to press against her husband's strong chest. She circled her arms around his neck, her fingers catching lightly at his curly hair. "What made you decide to come for me?" she asked.

"I didn't want to. I was afraid to risk more heart-break. But once I got in motion, I couldn't stop my-self. As bad as the dread was, the hope was more. I knew I couldn't live each day without you unless I gave winning you my best shot."

"When I saw you in the light from the fire, I thought I'd dreamed you. I was afraid you were a vision. And then when I realized it was really you, I thought I might faint from happiness."

"I love you, Celeste."

"And I love you. With all of the power of the past and the promise of the future." She lifted her lips for the kiss, and then gave herself to the luxury of her new husband.

OKAY, OKAY, that's the problem with these humans. They take things to the extreme. They finally get it right—because of moi—and now they want to coo and cuddle when the fiddlers are playing and the food is hot.

I suppose another road trip will be in order soon. It will be good to see Ashley and Brak, and especially Ayla. I'm sure Eleanor and Peter will be down from Washington to retrieve me. Home to my wonderful Clotilde and little Jordan.

And I leave behind me the Queen of the Gypsies and a happy union. James Bond couldn't have done it better.

But while these two bill and coo, I'm headed out to the fire and the music and the food. Remember, a man may work from sun to sun, but Familiar's work is never done.

Silhouette®

INTIMATE MOMENTS™
Sparked by danger, fueled by passion!

Passion.
Adventure.
Excitement.

Enter a world that's
larger than life, where
men and women overcome
life's greatest odds for
the ultimate prize: love.
Nonstop excitement is
closer than you think...in
Silhouette Intimate Moments!

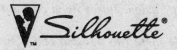

Silhouette®

Visit Silhouette Books at www.eHarlequin.com

SIMDIR104

♥ Silhouette®

♥ Silhouette®
SPECIAL EDITION™

Emotional, compelling stories that capture the intensity of living, loving and creating a family in today's world.

♥ Silhouette®
Desire

Modern, passionate reads that are powerful and provocative.

♥ Silhouette®
INTIMATE MOMENTS™

Romances that are sparked by danger and fueled by passion.

SILHOUETTE Romance®

From today to forever, these love stories offer today's woman fairytale romance.

♥ Silhouette®
BOMBSHELL

Action-filled romances with strong, sexy, savvy women who save the day.

eHARLEQUIN.com

The Ultimate Destination for Women's Fiction

Visit eHarlequin.com's Bookstore today for today's most popular books at great prices.

- An extensive selection of romance books by top authors!

- Choose our convenient "bill me" option. No credit card required.

- New releases, Themed Collections and hard-to-find backlist.

- A sneak peek at upcoming books.

- Check out book excerpts, book summaries and Reader Recommendations from other members and post your own too.

- Find out what everybody's reading in Bestsellers.

- Save BIG with everyday discounts and exclusive online offers!

- Our Category Legend will help you select reading that's exactly right for you!

- Visit our Bargain Outlet often for huge savings and special offers!

- Sweepstakes offers. Enter for your chance to win special prizes, autographed books and more.

Your purchases are 100% guaranteed—so shop online at www.eHarlequin.com today!

INTBB104R

eHARLEQUIN.com

The Ultimate Destination for Women's Fiction

Your favorite authors are just a click away
at www.eHarlequin.com!

- Take a sneak peek at the covers and
  read summaries of **Upcoming Books**

- Choose from over 600
  author **profiles!**

- Chat with your favorite authors
  on our **message boards.**

- Are you an author in the making?
  Get advice from published authors
  in **The Inside Scoop!**

Learn about your favorite authors
in a fun, interactive setting—
visit www.eHarlequin.com today!

INTAUTH04R

HARLEQUIN®
Live the emotion™

HARLEQUIN®
AMERICAN *Romance*®

Upbeat, All-American Romances

HARLEQUIN®
flipside

Romantic Comedy

Harlequin Historicals®
Historical Romantic Adventure!

HARLEQUIN®
INTRIGUE®

Romantic Suspense

HARLEQUIN®

HARLEQUIN ROMANCE®

The essence of modern romance

HARLEQUIN®
Presents

Seduction and Passion Guaranteed!

HARLEQUIN® Super ROMANCE®

Emotional, Exciting, Unexpected

Temptation®

Sassy, Sexy, Seductive!

www.eHarlequin.com   HDIR104

HARLEQUIN®
INTRIGUE®
WE'LL LEAVE YOU BREATHLESS!

If you've been looking for thrilling tales of
contemporary passion and sensuous love stories
with taut, edge-of-the-seat suspense—then
you'll love Harlequin Intrigue!

Every month, you'll meet six new heroes
who are guaranteed to make your spine tingle
and your pulse pound. With them you'll enter
into the exciting world of Harlequin Intrigue—
where your life is on the line
and so is your heart!

THAT'S INTRIGUE—
ROMANTIC SUSPENSE
AT ITS BEST!

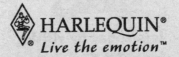

HARLEQUIN®
Live the emotion™

www.eHarlequin.com   INTDIR104

eHARLEQUIN.com

The Ultimate Destination for Women's Fiction

The eHarlequin.com online community is *the* place to share opinions, thoughts and feelings!

- Joining the community is easy, fun and **FREE!**

- Connect with **other romance fans** on our message boards.

- Meet your **favorite authors** without leaving home!

- **Share opinions** on books, movies, celebrities…and *more!*

Here's what our members say:

"I love the friendly and helpful atmosphere filled with support and humor."
—Texanna (eHarlequin.com member)

"Is this the place for me, or what? There is nothing I love more than 'talking' books, especially with fellow readers who are reading the same ones I am."
—Jo Ann (eHarlequin.com member)

Join today by visiting
www.eHarlequin.com!

INTCOMM04R